S320

INFECTIOUS DISEASE

OPEN UNIVERSITY

4

DIAGNOSING INFECTION

prepared for the Course Team by
Laura Hibberts and Hilary MacQueen

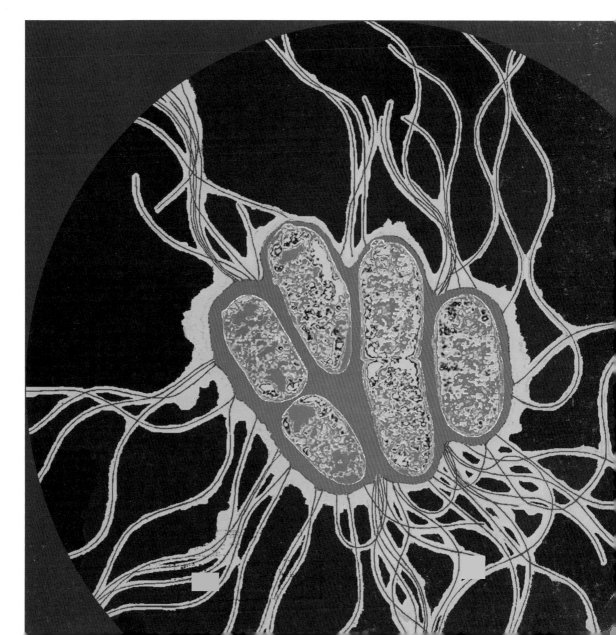

Cover picture: Coloured transmission electron micrograph of a cluster of *Salmonella* sp. bacteria. The cell at the centre is undergoing division, while the cells at centre left have just completed division.

This publication forms part of an Open University course S320 *Infectious Disease*. The complete list of texts which make up this course can be found at the back. Details of this and other Open University courses can be obtained from the Course Information and Advice Centre, PO Box 724, The Open University, Milton Keynes MK7 6ZS, United Kingdom: tel. +44 (0)1908 653231, e-mail general-enquiries@open.ac.uk

Alternatively, you may visit the Open University website at http://www.open.ac.uk where you can learn more about the wide range of courses and packs offered at all levels by The Open University.

To purchase a selection of Open University course materials visit the webshop at www.ouw.co.uk, or contact Open University Worldwide, Michael Young Building, Walton Hall, Milton Keynes MK7 6AA, United Kingdom for a brochure. tel. +44 (0)1908 858785; fax +44 (0)1908 858787; e-mail ouwenq@open.ac.uk

The Open University
Walton Hall, Milton Keynes
MK7 6AA

First published 2003.

Copyright © 2003 The Open University

Edited, designed and typeset by The Open University.

Printed and bound in the United Kingdom by the Alden Group, Oxford.

ISBN 0 7492 56583

1.1

THE S320 COURSE TEAM

Course Team Chair

Michael Gillman

Course Manager

Viki Burnage

Course Team Assistant

Dawn Partner

Course Team Authors

Basiro Davey (Books 1 & 7)

Tim Halliday (Book 5)

Paddy Farrington (Book 6)

Michael Gillman (Books 1 & 5)

Hilary MacQueen (Books 2 & 4)

David Male (Books 1, 3 & 7)

Consultant Authors

Eric Bowers (Book 2)

Christine Heading (Book 7)

Laura Hibberts (Books 2 & 4)

Ralph Muller (Book 7)

Editors

Pat Forster

Gilly Riley

Margaret Swithenby

Academic Reader

Mary Manley

External Course Assessor

Bo Drasar

OU Graphic Design

Roger Courthold

Sian Lewis

Video Editing

Wilf Eynon

Michael Francis

CD-ROM Production

Greg Black

Phil Butcher

BBC Production

Martin Kemp

Rights Executive

Christine Brady

Picture Research

Lydia Eaton

Indexer

Jean Macqueen

Course Websites

Patrina Law

Louise Olney

Sue Dugher

CONTENTS

INTRODUCTION

Although it is not exhaustive, this book should provide you with the necessary knowledge to understand most of the laboratory techniques used to diagnose common infectious diseases, including those that you encounter in your further reading and project research. The text is supported by an assessable video sequence on the *Reference* CD, which demonstrates many of the basic techniques used to handle microbes. This material should preferably be viewed after reading this introductory chapter, and you may like to revisit it from time to time as you work through the book. Altogether, this book should take you two study weeks to cover.

Now that you have met the agents that cause infectious diseases (Book 2) and looked at the human body's response to them (Book 3), you are ready to find out about the laboratory diagnosis of these diseases, which is the subject of this book. Laboratory diagnosis of infection is of course taken for granted in industrialized nations, but in the developing world it is a luxury enjoyed by only a few. It is a sobering fact that most serious infections occur in places where there is a shortage of laboratory facilities for diagnosing them. Unfortunately, basic clinical microbiology for developing nations has not yet been given priority status by governments or agencies in developed nations, or by the developing nations themselves (Archibald and Reller, 2001). Therefore, in addition to detailing the laboratory diagnosis of infectious diseases, this book will attempt to describe how such diseases may be diagnosed in the absence of such facilities.

We begin by considering the work of the laboratory as a whole, and the safety procedures employed. We then go on to detail the techniques used to detect and identify infectious agents. For reasons that should become clear as you read on, these are broadly divided into 'low-tech' and 'high-tech' methods. We then go on to look at the application of these methods in the real world, to diagnose some clinically important diseases.

1.1 Clinical diagnosis

Screening programs exist for the early detection of some diseases, such as cervical cancer, but usually the first stage in the diagnosis of a disease is the realization by the patient, or whoever looks after them, that something is wrong. The changes to the normal functioning of the body noticed by the patient are **symptoms**. In most cases, the ailment is easily recognized and treated by the patient, or their carer (for example, athlete's foot may be treated with over-the-counter anti-fungal powder), but on other occasions a consultation with a doctor may be required (Figure 1.1 overleaf). The doctor will take a **history** from the patient, including the symptoms and any recent travels, and together with the **signs** he or she observes, make an initial diagnosis. The signs observed by the doctor are those changes in the body that point towards disease, but are not apparent to the patient. These signs may be observed during a clinical examination or tested for later. They include features such as altered blood pressure, or changes in blood components.

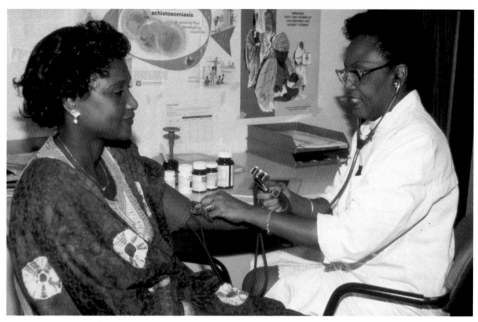

Figure 1.1 Consultation with a medical practitioner. The doctor (on the right) is measuring the patient's blood pressure.

The clinical diagnosis of a disease, based on the patient's history and a clinical examination, can be a difficult task.

○ Using your knowledge of infectious disease gained from your study of this course so far, suggest a diagnosis for a patient complaining of diarrhoea. What additional information would help you to identify the infectious agent responsible?

● Diarrhoea can be a symptom of cholera, cryptosporidiosis, salmonella, amoebiasis, giardiasis, *E. coli* O157 infection or travellers' diarrhoea (and many other diseases!). Additional information, such as the appearance of the faeces or stools, and the circumstances surrounding the onset and duration of the diarrhoea, would be important, as would be the presence of any other symptoms, such as fever. An understanding of the local epidemiology of diseases causing diarrhoea would be very important: for example, the diarrhoea is unlikely to be caused by cholera in an area where this disease is absent.

Many common symptoms are shared by a variety of diseases, as you have seen in the example above and in the case study of influenza in Book 1. Cold-like and flu-like symptoms can also herald the onset of diseases as diverse as malaria, measles, pertussis and of course the common cold and influenza. Sometimes the medical practitioner may observe a sign characteristic of a particular disease, such as Koplik's spots which indicate a measles infection (Book 2, Section 3.6.1). Some diseases can be ruled out because a patient may have been vaccinated against them. Other diseases, such as influenza, occur in seasonal epidemics, so the time of year may provide a clue. Finally, individual behaviour needs to be taken into account. This may be considered in terms of profession (for example, a worker in the sex industry is at a high risk of contracting an HIV infection), or in terms of leisure pursuit (for example, walkers in forested areas may become infected with the bacterium that causes Lyme disease).

A clinical examination and a history may be sufficient for diagnosis if the patient is suffering from a relatively harmless disease or one with obvious signs and symptoms, such as chickenpox. In the past, smallpox was readily identified by its characteristic rash and subsequent pockmarks. This was an important factor in the success of the WHO's smallpox eradication programme, since it allowed rapid identification and isolation of smallpox victims. The control of smallpox was significantly improved by the imposition of **quarantine**, a means of limiting the exposure of healthy people to a disease by isolating infected individuals for a time. The word 'quarantine' derives from the French *quarantaine*, meaning a 40-day period, which was judged sufficiently long to prevent the spread of smallpox.

Not all diseases are so easily recognized, and further tests may be needed to confirm the doctor's suspicions, or to provide more information on which to work towards a diagnosis. The results of such tests provide further signs that may point toward a particular disease. There is a whole host of tests that can be performed, such as blood chemistry examinations and radiological investigations, but this book focuses mainly on those investigations that are usually carried out in a clinical (i.e. relating to disease) microbiology laboratory. These tests can provide evidence of infection by identifying either a causative agent of infectious disease (or that agent's components), or a specific host response provoked by such an agent.

1.2 Taking samples for laboratory diagnosis

These clinical tests require samples or specimens, which consist of material originating from the patient such as urine, faeces, pus, etc. A variety of methods exist for obtaining specimens, such as swabs, needle aspirate (drawing of fluids from the body with a hypodermic needle), expectoration (coughing up sputum from the lower respiratory tract), using tubes introduced into passages or organs, and **biopsies** (removal of living tissue for examination). The local medical practitioner, or their support staff, will be able to take many of these samples, but for those requiring more invasive techniques, anaesthesia may be required. Biopsies, for example, are normally taken in hospital.

Every effort is made when sampling to obtain only the material of interest.

○ From what you have learned so far, how likely is it that a clinical sample will contain, along with human material, just the causative agent of an infection?

◐ It is very unlikely that a sample will contain just the infective agent, since the skin, mucous membranes and especially the intestines, have a rich commensal flora, which will contaminate a sample. (It is also possible that the sample will not contain an infectious agent at all if the patient's illness has a different, non-infectious cause.)

A detailed knowledge of the commensal flora that is likely to grow along with the causative agent is therefore essential if laboratory tests are to be interpreted correctly. However, samples obtained from sites that normally contain just human material, such as cerebrospinal fluid (CSF) and blood, may well contain the causative organism alone. Since these sites lack a commensal flora, the isolation of *any* organism from one of them is treated as significant.

Sterile containers and equipment are used for sample collection, to avoid the introduction of any extraneous organisms. Within reason, 'the larger the better' is a good rule of thumb for specimens. If a large quantity of pus has been produced, it is better to send a generous sample than simply a swab of it for analysis. Swabs dipped in material make much poorer specimens than a sizeable sample, simply because there is less chance of finding the agent of a disease. For example, a swab dipped in faeces is likely to pick up many orders of magnitude more commensals than pathogens, and subsequent identification of the pathogen might be more difficult. If possible, the sample should be taken before any treatment with drugs that kill infectious agents, such as antibiotics, has begun.

○ Why is this important?

● If treatment with antibiotics has begun, the infectious agent may have been inactivated and may not be detectable in a sample.

Specimens are sent to the laboratory as quickly as possible, so that the causative agent will still be **viable** (able to replicate or divide) when it gets there, and not overwhelmed by the growth of contaminating microbes. A variety of techniques are used to achieve these aims and to mitigate the effects of any delay in reaching the laboratory. Some strict anaerobic bacteria require the use of special sampling equipment that excludes air, in order for them to remain viable. Carefully designed **transport media** are often employed: samples suspected of containing viruses are transported in media containing buffered salts and **serum** along with antibiotics to prevent the growth of fungi or bacteria. Serum (plural: sera) is the part of the blood left behind after cells, platelets and fibrinogen have all been removed, usually by clotting. **Plasma** is similar to serum in that it is the liquid portion of the blood, but it still contains fibrinogen.

It may seem obvious to mention that the choice of sample is crucial for an effective diagnosis to be made, since it is unlikely that the infectious agent will be identified if the wrong site is sampled. The choice of sampling site depends on the medical practitioner's initial assessment. For example, if a *Chlamydia* infection is suspected, a cervical swab may be taken; if a protoctist is implicated, then a faecal sample might be the most appropriate. The tests performed on the samples will be determined by the probable nature of the causative organism; that is, whether a bacterium, virus, fungus, protoctist or invertebrate parasite is suspected. Although certain organisms will be routinely sought in a particular type of sample, a search for unusual microbes, or any additional tests, must be specially requested. Sometimes it isn't obvious what the likely causative agent could be: a patient complaining of fever and joint pain might be suffering from an infection of the lining of the heart, known as endocarditis. A blood sample is needed in this case, and promptly too, since the condition can be rapidly fatal without the administration of antimicrobial drugs.

1.3 The clinical microbiology laboratory

Time may be a crucial factor in the clinical microbiology laboratory: if the test results are to influence the treatment of a critically ill patient, then they must be available quickly. Sometimes, treatment is started even before results are received, and the data are then used to confirm that appropriate treatment has been given.

This may happen because the patient's life is in danger; for example, if the person is believed to have bacterial meningitis, antibiotic therapy is administered before confirmation of this diagnosis. Similarly, in non-emergency cases (e.g. urinary tract infection) where a laboratory test is only required for confirmation, the patient may be started on antibiotics immediately. However, where the causative agent of infection *can* be identified before treatment begins, inappropriate treatment with antibiotics (e.g. for patients infected with a virus) may be avoided. It is also important to identify pathogens that may cause serious epidemics, so that appropriate preventative measures may be taken at the level of the population, as well as for the individual.

Clinical specimens arriving at the microbiology laboratory are delivered to the specimen reception. Here each sample is checked against the accompanying record card, its entry recorded and its analysis prioritized according to the urgency with which the result is required. Good documentation is essential, since errors may have legal as well as medical repercussions, for example if the sample is to be subjected to forensic or epidemiological analysis. In practice, both the specimen and record card are given a unique identification number. If specimens are not examined immediately, they must be stored appropriately so that the requested tests will still be valid. For example, specimens may need to be refrigerated at 4 °C or below, to prevent deterioration. Once the specimens have arrived, they can then be subjected to the particular tests requested by the doctor. Some of these tests involve procedures that are quite straightforward and do not require much in the way of sophisticated equipment. Others, however, may require a well equipped laboratory with modern, expensive kit and reagents. These facilities are only found in some of the richest countries, and although the simpler, cheaper techniques are more generally available worldwide, even they are beyond the reach of some countries. We look at each group of techniques below.

1.4 Notifiable diseases

In 1889, some diseases such as cholera and diphtheria were declared notifiable for the first time in Britain. This meant that cases had to be reported to the authorities by law, and appropriate action could then be taken to prevent their spread. Today the list of notifiable infectious diseases in England and Wales has grown to around 30, and countries all over the world have their own lists of notifiable diseases – the USA has 58. The lists vary from country to country, but the principle is the same. The WHO operates an equivalent system on a global scale called Communicable Disease Surveillance and Response (CSR), but this system is voluntary. (This list is available from the Book 4 online resources.) However, WHO Member States are legally required to notify plague, cholera and yellow fever as part of the International Health Regulations (IHR). These regulations were set up to allow a rapid and coordinated international response to serious communicable diseases.

When a clinical microbiology laboratory identifies a single case of one of the notifiable diseases, the authorities must be informed immediately, so that suitable measures to prevent spread can be put into action. Of course, the physician who requested the sample, and the patient, must also be informed, so that the individual treatment – which may include strict hygiene practices and quarantine – can be started straight away.

BASIC LABORATORY TECHNIQUES

At some point during your study of this chapter you should view the video sequence *Microbiology Techniques* on the *Reference* CD.

Before going into the details of diagnostic tests, we need to introduce two concepts that affect such tests: sensitivity and specificity. **Sensitivity** is a measure of how much (or how little) of a sample needs to be analysed before a clear-cut result is obtained. A highly sensitive test requires only a small amount of sample to yield a result. **Specificity** relates to the accuracy of the recognition between the test reagent and the patient's sample. You are familiar with this concept from immunology, where there is high specificity of antigen–antibody recognition. When considering a test reagent, it is important to bear these two parameters in mind. A specific reagent is not always very sensitive: if the antibody has a low affinity for the antigen, for example, a lot of it may be needed for a positive result to be apparent. In this case, the incidence of **false negatives**, that is, samples that give a negative result in a diagnostic test even though they contain the disease agent, may be significant. On the other hand, if a test is highly sensitive but lacks specificity, it may give rise to **false positives** – positive results where no infection exists. Both these types of error can have serious consequences for the patient, and people who manufacture and use test materials have to be aware of these pitfalls.

☐ Suggest a precaution that should be taken every time a diagnostic test is carried out.

▨ Both a positive and a negative control should be included in each batch of tests.

If you are unfamiliar with the concept of controls, read Box 2.1.

Box 2.1   Positive and negative controls

In order to interpret the results of tests or experiments, it is often necessary to compare the results against known standards. Because conditions may vary slightly from one experiment to another, the best plan is to include these standards each time the experiment or test is carried out. Such internal standards are known as **controls**. Controls replicate exactly all but one of the conditions of the experiments, but are 'fixed' in such a way that the result is known beforehand, by manipulating one component of the experiment. For example, a vital reagent (a chemical involved in a reaction) may be omitted, so that the result will be zero – the experiment will definitely not work, and any value obtained from the test system will be the baseline against which all the other results can be measured. Such a control is called a **negative control**. On the other hand, it is also useful to have an idea of what the result should be if the experiment definitely has worked – a **positive control**. A positive control includes a known amount of material that will give a positive result in the test, often called a **reference sample**. A reference sample could replace, for example, a patient's sample; in all other respects, the control would be the same as the tests. Knowing the amount of reference sample in the positive control allows the test results to be more quantitative.

2.1 Laboratory safety

A clinical microbiology laboratory handles human material that is likely to contain infectious agents, and although particular agents may be suspected, the presence of additional unexpected infectious agents cannot be ruled out. The author can remember culturing a stool sample from a student that unexpectedly turned out to harbour *Salmonella typhi*, the causative agent of typhoid fever! These clinical specimens are therefore treated with great respect; safety procedures are rigorously enforced and must comply with the local health and safety rules. In the UK these rules come from the COSHH (Control of Substances Hazardous to Health) regulations, which govern the codes of practice in force in all workplaces, not just clinical microbiology laboratories.

It is important that infectious agents are contained, and not allowed to escape into the environment, where they might pose a risk to the public. The days when microbiologists would work during lunch with specimens and sandwiches on the same bench are thankfully long gone. Nowadays, eating, drinking, smoking or application of cosmetics in a microbiology laboratory are forbidden. Specially designed white coats are worn, which you will see when you view the video sequence. These coats, with their high necks and close cuffs, afford more protection than the 'traditional' white coat, and are removed before leaving the laboratory. Correct use of such coats ensures that culture material does not come into contact with clothes. Workers must also wash their hands thoroughly before they leave the laboratory. Additionally, all materials that have come into contact with cultures are either disinfected, or sterilized in an **autoclave** (a machine that exposes materials to steam at high temperature and pressure) prior to disposal.

Finally, when a microbe is being cultivated in the laboratory, the culture needs to be kept free of other microbes, since their presence would invalidate any test results obtained. Such contaminant-free cultures are described as *pure*. The requirements for containment and maintaining cultures in a pure state are met by using laboratory safety procedures including **aseptic technique**. A great deal of the work in routine diagnostic laboratories is carried out on open bench-tops, using aseptic techniques. You have already come across the term 'aseptic' in connection with the mucociliary escalator of the respiratory tract, where it was defined as 'free from disease-causing organisms'. Here, its meaning is different, since clinical microbiology is all about working with disease-causing organisms! Aseptic in this context means 'uncontaminated with microbes from other sources'. Aseptic techniques are a lot easier to understand if you can see them for yourself, and you will see examples of them when you view the associated video material. The techniques may seem tedious but they are crucial in maintaining the safety of laboratory workers and the reliability of the tests they carry out. Once you have viewed the techniques on the video sequence, you will be better equipped to understand the practical procedures described below.

The **Bunsen burner** (see Figure 2.1), which you may be familiar with from school science lessons, is crucial to many aseptic manipulations. It is a small laboratory burner consisting of a vertical metal tube connected to a gas source and produces a flame from a mixture of the gas and air which is let in through an adjustable hole at the base of the instrument. The hot blue flame, obtained by opening the Bunsen's airhole fully, is the one used for these techniques. Aseptic technique is especially important in minimizing the production of **aerosols**. Aerosols are small drops of airborne liquid or solid that can be breathed in, and if they contain pathogenic

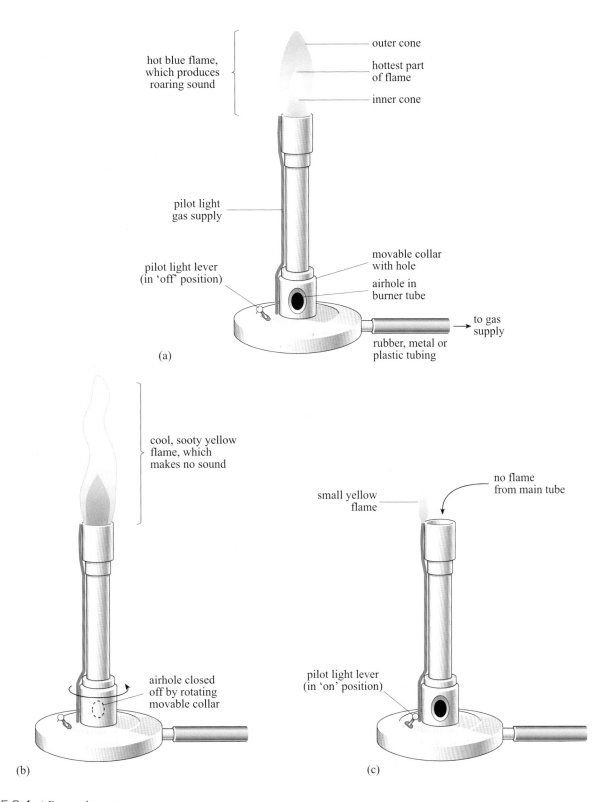

outer cone

hottest part of flame

inner cone

hot blue flame, which produces roaring sound

pilot light gas supply

pilot light lever (in 'off' position)

movable collar with hole

airhole in burner tube

to gas supply

rubber, metal or plastic tubing

(a)

cool, sooty yellow flame, which makes no sound

airhole closed off by rotating movable collar

(b)

no flame from main tube

small yellow flame

pilot light lever (in 'on' position)

(c)

FIGURE 2.1 A Bunsen burner.
(a) The burner with its airhole fully open. The hot, blue flame is used for aseptic manipulations.
(b) The burner with its airhole fully closed. The yellow flame is more easily visible than the blue flame or the pilot light.
(c) Using the pilot light.

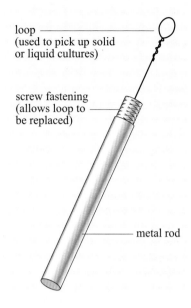

loop
(used to pick up solid
or liquid cultures)

screw fastening
(allows loop to
be replaced)

metal rod

FIGURE 2.2 A bacteriologist's loop.

microbes, can thus infect laboratory workers. For this reason, containers of liquid broths (prone to aerosol production) are 'flamed', by placing their open necks in the flame of a Bunsen burner. The updraft created by the flame carries aerosols up and away from the worker, and the microbes present are burned in the flame. The hottest part of the blue flame is also used to sterilize equipment, such as the **bacteriologist's loop** (shown in Figure 2.2), a small rod into one end of which a thin, flexible looped wire, is inserted. Bacteriologist's loops are used to handle solid and liquid cultures, and are flamed many times during manipulations. Because the wire is very thin, it transfers heat rapidly, so the loop heats up and cools down quickly. Plastic disposable loops are also available, but using them is a more expensive option.

Not all organisms can be safely manipulated on the open bench, and in fact microbes can be classified according to the safety procedures required when working with them. In Table 2.1, containment refers to the use of safety cabinets, which are glass-fronted cabinets used for manipulation of cultures (Figure 2.3a). The cabinets isolate the worker from the culture material more effectively than using a Bunsen burner on the open bench. All material – including samples, cultures and equipment – that is a potential source of infection should be labelled with tape bearing a 'biohazard' symbol (Figure 2.3b).

TABLE 2.1 Classification of biological agents in the UK; other countries have equivalent systems.

Group	Safety measures	Description
1 e.g. *Saccharomyces cerevisiae*	Standard laboratory procedures	Unlikely to cause human disease.
2 e.g. most influenza viruses	Limited access Partial containment to prevent escape of airborne agents	Can cause human disease and may be a hazard to employees; it is unlikely to spread to the community and there is usually effective prophylaxis or treatment available.
3 e.g. *Mycobacterium tuberculosis*	Controlled access Partial containment for all tasks	Can cause severe human disease and may be a serious hazard to employees; it may spread to the community, but there is usually effective prophylaxis or treatment available.
4 e.g. Ebola virus	Controlled access Maximum containment equipment Special self-contained suits with separate air supply	Causes severe human disease and is a serious hazard to employees; it is likely to spread to the community and there is usually no effective prophylaxis or treatment available.

FIGURE 2.3
(a) A safety cabinet. Lids can be removed from sample tubes without risk of contamination. (b) The COSSH biohazard symbol, which is used to indicate the presence of biological material that is likely to be infectious.

(a)

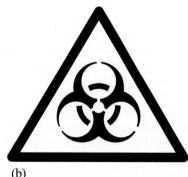

(b)

2.2 Isolation of microbes

Isolation describes the separation of a specific microbe from material, the exact microbial content of which is unknown. In clinical microbiology, particular pathogens will be sought from patient specimens, but in order to do this, material from the patient is used for **culture**. *Culture*, in this context, is the growing of microbes in a nutrient medium, where the term *growth* refers to an increase in size or number: recall that bacteria grow and then divide, whereas viruses simply replicate.

2.2.1 Culture media

Growing a pathogen in the laboratory is a useful part of diagnosing the cause of an infectious disease, and is an essential step for some further tests such as determining the antibiotic sensitivities of bacteria. The growth media and equipment are sterilized before use, so that the only microbes that grow are the ones introduced deliberately. Sterilization is carried out using an autoclave, which kills all known organisms and inactivates viruses, using high-pressure steam. Bacteria will grow on artificial media, which may be solid (called agars, singular **agar**) or liquid (called **broths**), and there is a huge range of artificial growth media available (see Table 2.2 for some examples). Solid media owe their solidity to a gelling agent, agar, which is a polysaccharide extracted from particular seaweeds. Agar has a number of useful properties, but the most important is that it is indigestible to most bacteria and doesn't end up liquefied by their growth, which used to happen to its predecessor, gelatin.

TABLE 2.2 Examples of some common growth media.

Name	Composition	Selective agent	Indicator system	Use
nutrient broth	based on a water extract of meat with added peptone*	none	none	general-purpose, non-selective medium
nutrient agar	as above but solidified by the addition of agar	as above	as above	as above
fresh blood agar	nutrient agar with added whole blood from horse	none	blood allows production of haemolysins to be detected	rich, general-purpose medium
MacConkey's agar	nutrient agar with lactose, bile salts and NaCl	bile salts	lactose and neutral red pH indicator	isolation of salmonellae and shigellae
VCAT agar	rich medium incorporating lysed blood (releases more nutrients than whole blood)	antimicrobial agents: vancomycin, colistin, amphotericin B, trimethoprim	none	used for growing *Neisseria gonorrhoeae*
mannitol salt agar	nutrient agar containing NaCl	NaCl	mannitol and phenol red pH indicator	isolation of staphylococci

* The term *peptone* is used to describe partially digested protein.

Artificial media comprise a mineral base, a nitrogen source, a carbon source and an energy source (many microbes can use a single organic compound as a source of both energy and carbon). The mineral base is composed of all the nutrients that can be supplied to bacteria in inorganic form. Depending on the organism to be grown, other substances, collectively known as *growth factors*, are included. These are organic compounds required by an organism, that it is unable to synthesize itself from simpler carbon sources. Growth factors are usually amino acids, vitamins or DNA and RNA precursors. If the medium is made of chemically defined nutrients, whose exact composition is known, then it is described as a **defined medium**. Undefined or **complex media**, on the other hand, have a chemical composition that is not precisely known, since they contain variable components such as yeast extract or partially hydrolysed protein extracts. Complex media tend to be richer than defined media, and are consequently able to support the growth of a wider range of bacteria.

As has already been mentioned, samples of material from a patient are unlikely to contain just the causative agent of a disease. The pathogen responsible (if there is one) is likely to comprise only a small proportion of the microbes that can be cultured from such a sample; it really is like looking for a needle in a haystack! This problem is overcome by manipulating the culture conditions in favour of the suspected pathogen by exploiting its particular characteristics, for example the ability to grow in the presence of certain inhibitory substances. If the pathogen is present, it will then be able to grow more easily than the other microbes, and become more abundant relative to them. A medium designed to favour the growth of one organism over another, is described as a **selective medium** if it is solid, and as an **enrichment medium** if it is a liquid. For example, MacConkey's agar selects for intestinal bacteria because it contains bile salts, which inhibit many other types of bacteria.

○ Taking into account the natural environments where *Vibrio cholerae* bacteria are found (refer back to the Cholera Case Study if necessary), can you suggest how a growth medium might be made selective for them?

● A growth medium could be made selective for *V. cholerae* by the addition of sodium chloride, since the bacteria are found naturally in saltwater, which kills many other pathogens.

When we turn to the diagnosis of cholera infection later in this book, you will find that sodium chloride is indeed used as a selective agent for this bacterium.

The pH of a medium can also be used to make it selective. For example, one of the distinguishing features of cholera vibrios is their ability to grow at alkaline pH, so making a growth medium alkaline, renders it selective for these bacteria. The incubation conditions are also selective: obligate anaerobes will be killed in the presence of oxygen, whereas obligate aerobes will die without it. In fact *all* growth media and incubation conditions are selective to some extent.

Growth media can also be used to determine the presence of organisms with particular biochemical pathways, allowing for rapid 'one-step' identification of particular pathogens in samples. This is achieved by the addition of **indicators**. These are reagents that, by a colour change or another characteristic property, demonstrate whether a specific substance is present or absent, or give a measure of the substance's concentration, or quantify the extent to which a chemical reaction has occurred. For example, MacConkey's agar contains a pH indicator called – perhaps misleadingly – neutral red (which is red in acid) and the sugar lactose as an indicator system. Colonies that are able to metabolize lactose reduce the pH, and so appear red, while those unable to do so appear a buff colour. This system allows faecal pathogens such as salmonellae to be distinguished from other aerobes of the normal commensal flora found in the bowel, since salmonellae do not ferment lactose and so remain buff-coloured. The use of MacConkey's agar illustrates two other important points: first, a growth medium may be *both* a selective *and* an indicator medium; and second, organisms affect their environment (the pH in this case) as they grow.

Fungi can also be grown using artificial media, but only solid media are used, since the fungal growth obtained in broth cultures is generally unsuitable for diagnostic investigations. In contrast to the fungi, some protoctists can produce suitable growth in broth cultures. The main differences between fungal and bacterial culture are that fungi may take up to three weeks to grow, instead of the overnight incubation sufficient for most bacteria, and that fungi are grown on media with an acid pH, as opposed to the neutral or alkaline conditions favoured by most bacteria.

☐ Can you recall from your study of Book 2 how viruses are grown in the laboratory and explain why?

▨ Viruses are cultivated in tissue culture, fertilized chicken eggs, or laboratory animals, since they cannot replicate outside living cells.

A variety of cells are used for tissue culture, with particular types of cell used for the replication of particular types of virus. This is partly to do with the tropism of the virus, and partly to do with the availability of cell lines of various types which grow well in the laboratory and in which the virus will readily replicate.

Once **inoculation** (deliberate introduction of material into sterile medium) has occurred, the media are incubated at 37 °C, until evidence of growth is seen. Growth is assessed by the appearance of colonies of bacteria or fungi on agar, cloudiness in broths, or cytopathic effects such as plaques in virally infected tissue culture cells.

Pure cultures, containing cells of only one type, such as a particular strain of bacterial species, are required for laboratory tests. Pure cultures can be obtained by growing material on solid media such that single colonies are obtained, by the streak-plate method, which you saw demonstrated in the *Microbiology Techniques* video sequence.

☐ A non-selective medium is used to check for purity. Suggest why this is the case.

▨ On a selective medium, only the chosen microbe will grow. However, contaminants may also be present, even though they are unable to grow to produce visible colonies. On a non-selective medium, even contaminating microbes will grow.

The culture is spread over the surface of the agar until single, well separated cells are obtained. Upon incubation, these single cells grow and divide until the material produced becomes visible to the naked eye. These visible growths are called colonies and the cell that seeded each one is referred to as a **colony forming unit** or **cfu**. However, some bacteria are found in clusters or pairs, and in these cases, a single cluster of cells represents a colony forming unit. Each colony contains cells that are identical to one another, although they may be different from those of neighbouring colonies.

The rate of cell growth and division required to produce visible colonies from a single invisible cell in a matter of hours is phenomenal: the doubling time under optimum conditions for a bacterium can be as little as 20 minutes.

○ For an incubation period lasting 12 hours, calculate the maximum number of cell divisions that can occur for a single bacterium.

● If doubling time is as short as 20 minutes, there can be three rounds of cell division an hour, so there will be $3 \times 12 = 36$ cell divisions in 12 hours.

○ How many cells will be present at the end of this time?

● 2 to the power 36, which is $2^{36} = 6.87 \times 10^{10}$ cells.

○ Assuming for simplicity that a bacterial colony is a cylinder 1 mm high and that a bacterial cell is an oblong block with the dimensions $0.5 \, \mu m \times 0.5 \, \mu m \times 2 \, \mu m$, calculate the diameter of the colony that will be produced. (Volume of a cylinder = $\pi r^2 h$, where r is the radius and h the height.)

● Rearranging the formula for the volume of a cylinder,

$$r = \sqrt{\frac{\text{volume}}{\pi h}}$$

Volume of the colony = number of cells × volume of each cell

$$= 6.87 \times 10^{10} \times 0.5 \, \mu m \times 0.5 \, \mu m \times 2 \, \mu m$$
$$= 3.44 \times 10^{10} \, \mu m^3$$

Therefore

$$r = \sqrt{\frac{3.44 \times 10^{10} \, \mu m^3}{3.14 \times 10^3 \, \mu m}} = \sqrt{1.1 \times 10^7 \, \mu m^2} \approx 3.3 \text{ mm}$$

So the diameter is 6.6 mm, which is an easily visible, large colony.

One of these single colonies can then be used to grow a pure culture. The spreading out of culture in this way on an agar plate is termed **plating out**. Plating out is also used to check the purity of broth cultures (see *Microbiology Techniques* video sequence).

2.2.2 Drug sensitivity testing

Sometimes it is important to identify the antibiotics that will kill, or prevent the growth of, a bacterium. This is most easily achieved using small paper discs impregnated with antibiotic. The bacterial culture under test is plated out in such a way that it will grow all over the plate without any gaps. This type of confluent growth is called a **lawn**. Prior to incubation, the antibiotic discs are placed on the agar, and during incubation the antibiotics diffuse out of their discs into the surrounding area. Where a bacterium is sensitive to an antibiotic, a circular **zone of inhibition**, where the bacterium could not grow, is observed following incubation. If the bacterium is resistant to an antibiotic, then it will grow right up to the disc.

2.3 Non-culture methods of diagnosis

Culturing microbes is not always a suitable means of diagnosis, since some microbes are difficult to grow, or take a long time to produce visible colonies. The culturing of viruses is particularly time-consuming and expensive. Luckily, there are other strategies that require neither culture nor high-tech methods, yet which can provide a diagnosis. We look at two such methods now.

2.3.1 Macroscopic and microscopic examination

Sometimes simply looking at a specimen with the unaided eye can provide some information; for example, a transparent urine sample is unlikely to contain bacteria that cause urinary tract infections. Further information can be obtained using an ordinary light microscope to examine the sample material. A small portion of the sample is placed in a drop of water on a microscope slide, and covered with a thin square sheet of glass called a coverslip (see Figure 2.4). The sample is then described as mounted, and this type of mount is referred to as a **wet mount**. Urine, faeces, CSF and other liquid samples can all be examined in this way. Most microbes do not show up well in a wet mount, and need to be stained using chemicals. Prior to staining, sample material is allowed to dry on the slide and is then stuck or **fixed** to the slide using heat or alcohol. This prevents the material being washed off the slide during the staining process. The most common stains used for bacteria are the Gram stain and a variety of stains for acid-fast bacteria.

○   If you suspected a patient had tuberculosis, which stain would you use?

●   The Ziehl–Neelsen stain (see Book 2, Section 2.2)

Other microbes, such as protoctists and fungi, may require specialized staining techniques. Light microscopy is a cheap and rapid diagnostic tool, but unsuitable for observing viruses. With the exception of poxviruses, these can only be seen using electron microscopy, which is an expensive and lengthy procedure.

2.3.2 Serology

Serology is the study of antigens and antibodies in patients' sera. The effectiveness of serological techniques depends on the *interactions* of antigens and antibodies, and these methods have been, and continue to be, very important for diagnosis. As you have seen, in some instances it is not possible to culture a microbe, and molecular methods of investigation (see Chapter 3) may be unavailable. In these circumstances, the evidence of infection may be sought in the patient's blood, where a rise in the level of antibodies to a specific infectious agent would indicate that an immune response to that agent has taken place. This type of investigation requires two blood samples to be taken from the patient: one early on in the infection (called the *acute* serum), and another 10–14 days later (called the *convalescent* serum). During this period, a large increase in the level of antibody specific for the pathogen is produced (see Book 3, Chapter 2). The size of the increase varies between individuals, so an arbitrary level is taken as significant.

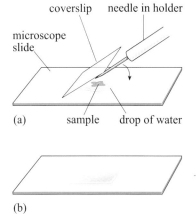

Figure 2.4
Preparation of a wet mount.
(a) Using a needle set into a wooden handle, the coverslip is lowered onto the sample material.
(b) The sample spreads out thinly under the coverslip and the wet mount is now ready to be examined under the microscope.

A fourfold increase in specific antibody levels is known as **seroconversion**, and indicates that the patient has suffered an acute infection. However, with this method, diagnosis is only possible retrospectively. Evidence of long-term chronic infections may also be obtained by testing the patient's blood for the presence of specific antibody, as you will see in Section 4.2. Since such infections are chronic rather than acute, the comparison of acute and convalescent sera cannot be made, so other criteria are used for interpreting the results.

Serological methods include testing for the presence of specific antibodies in a patient's serum, indicating that they have been exposed to a particular pathogen and have mounted an immune response to it, but also include tests for the *current* presence of the pathogen in the blood. This involves using so-called test sera, a collection of standard sera known to contain antibodies to particular species, or even strains, of pathogens. Here the patient's blood is tested for the presence of particular pathogen-specific *antigens*. Don't make the mistake of thinking that serology always involves looking for *antibodies* in the patient's serum.

One of the most commonly used serological tests is the **haemagglutination test**. As well as being used in blood typing, where non-matched bloods cause the red cells to clump, it is used to detect pathogens that carry haemagglutinin on their surfaces.

○ Which types of pathogen have surface haemagglutinins?

● Some bacteria, such as *Bordetella pertussis* and *Helicobacter pylori*, have them, and so does the influenza virus.

Haemagglutinins clump red cells by cross-linking their plasma membranes via specific receptor molecules (see Figure 2.5a). Standard numbers of red cells are exposed in small wells in a *microtitre plate*, to the patient's serum or to stock viral samples as a positive control. (A microtitre plate is a small plastic tray containing a number of wells, where each well acts like a tiny test-tube. These trays allow a large number of reactions to be performed all at once using the minimum of reagents.) If the red cells are unaffected by the serum, they fall to the bottom of the well and form a tight red pellet. However, if they clump, they remain as a 'mat' within the well. It is easy to distinguish these two patterns visually. The presence of a mat in the test well indicates the presence of haemagglutinin-producing organisms in the patient's sample, and is indicative of disease. The result of a haemagglutination test is shown in Figure 2.5b.

The haemagglutination test is so easy to carry out and interpret that it has been adapted for use in the diagnosis of diseases whose pathogens do not carry haemagglutinins. In some cases, it is possible to coat the surfaces of red cells with an antigen derived from elsewhere (such as a pathogen). If the patient's serum contains antibodies that bind to this antigen, then the coated red cells will be cross-linked as before, but this time by antibodies, not by, for example, viral haemagglutinin.

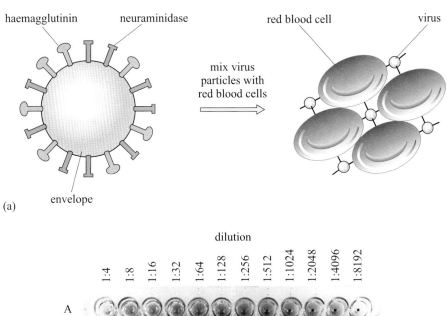

(a)

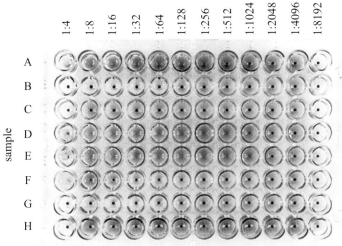

(b)

FIGURE 2.5 (a) Mechanism of haemagglutination by influenza virus. (b) Result of a haemagglutination test for influenza virus in a microtitre plate. Test samples are diluted serially so that a rough estimate of the amount of haemagglutinin in the sample can be made. Row A is the positive control. At the lower dilutions, where the reference sample is more concentrated, the red cells have formed a mat, indicating that they have been clumped by haemagglutinins. At the higher dilutions, containing less haemagglutinin, a pellet is starting to form, and at the highest dilution, 1 : 8192, the result is frankly negative. Indeed, at this dilution all the samples on the plate are so dilute as to give a negative result. Row B is the negative control. All the wells show a red cell pellet, indicating no haemagglutination. Rows C to H are test samples, some of which are positive and some negative. Note that sometimes the lowest dilution (highest amount of sample) appears negative, though other dilutions may be positive. This is for technical reasons involving overloading the reaction well with an excess of protein, and emphasizes the need to carry out several dilutions for each sample.

HIGH-TECH DIAGNOSTIC TECHNIQUES

The techniques described in Chapter 2 are generally simple and cheap enough to be used in laboratories throughout the world. However, there are limits to what can be achieved using them. As you have just seen, different types of cells are used for tissue culture, and they have to be grown for several weeks until there are enough to use for virus culture. This requires a high degree of technical expertise and special equipment, and the cells may be lost at any stage if they become contaminated with other microbes. Other pathogens may be impossible to grow *in vitro*, such as *Treponema pallidum* or hepatitis C virus, or just so dangerous that it is inadvisable to grow them outside specialist research facilities; one such is Ebola virus. In these circumstances, either secreted material such as toxins may be detected instead (although *T. pallidum* and hepatitis C virus do not produce them), or very sensitive techniques may be used to allow laboratory staff to work with the material available. Such techniques are described as *molecular methods* since they operate at the level of molecules such as DNA, and results from tests that employ these methods can be generated very fast. It is now possible to identify specific structural components of microbes using monoclonal antibodies raised specifically against them (see Box 3.1 overleaf) and to detect particular DNA and RNA sequences. For instance, DNA encoding particular antibiotic resistance genes may be identified in clinical samples. For example, *rpoB* mutants of *Mycobacterium tuberculosis*, which are resistant to rifampicin (Gilbert, 2002), have been detected. The levels of detection using these tests has been improved significantly since the 1990s, when the polymerase chain reaction (PCR) came into more general use (see Section 3.5). Amazingly, these techniques are now so sensitive that bacterial DNA in human bones that are thousands of years old can be detected. The DNA of *M. tuberculosis*, for example, has been detected in bones from 3000 BC (see Tuberculosis Case Study), but the researchers featured in the TV programme *In Search of Syphilis* were not so successful when they tried to find the DNA of *Treponema pallidum* in the bones of Rivenhall woman. In research, results are never guaranteed!

We now turn to look at some of these new techniques, which have two things in common: first, they exploit our recent molecular understanding of pathobiology, and, second, that they are relatively expensive and require sophisticated equipment to carry out, so are beyond the means of many developing countries. Nevertheless, their high sensitivity and specificity have often resulted in their being adopted as the **gold standard** (the test against which all others are measured) for the diagnosis of certain diseases.

3.1 Immunofluorescence

The first technique that we consider might not at first sight appear very sophisticated, as it is basically a microscopical technique. However, it uses a sophisticated microscope with an ultraviolet (uv) light source and expensive filters to detect fluorescence of labelled antibodies that have bound to cells or molecules in the test sample, and is not a technique that can readily be carried out in the field.

Box 3.1   Production of monoclonal antibodies

Many of the tests described in this chapter require laboratory antibodies, as opposed to patient-derived antibodies, but where do these antibodies come from? Such antibodies can be obtained by injecting laboratory animals with a purified antigen, on several occasions over a period of time. This procedure elicits a primary and then a secondary immune response, so that many antibodies to the purified antigen are found in the animal's blood. Such blood is said to have a high **antibody titre** (American spelling: titer). If blood is withdrawn from the animal and allowed to clot, its serum can be obtained, and since this serum has a high titre of the desired antibodies, it is known as **antiserum**.

Obtaining antibodies in this way has several drawbacks:

- The antiserum contains other antibodies besides those that recognize the purified antigen, and eliminating these unwanted immunoglobulins is difficult.
- The antibodies also vary in their antigen binding sites, depending on the particular epitope of the purified antigen that they bind. For this reason, such antibodies are described as **polyspecific**.
- Finally, the exact composition of the antiserum varies from batch to batch.

In the late 1970s, antibody production was revolutionized when batches of antibody with binding sites for only one epitope, or **monospecific** antibodies, became available. These antibodies were prepared by injecting laboratory animals with purified antigen and waiting for the subsequent rise in antibody titer. The spleens of these animals were then removed. The spleen is a site of maturation of B lymphocytes, and these cells were separated out from the tissue and fused with myeloma cells. The latter are cancerous B lymphocytes, which are immortal in cell culture, in contrast to ordinary B lymphocytes, which die after a few days in culture. (Mutant myeloma cells unable to produce antibodies themselves were used.) Fusing these two cell types produced a hybrid cell known as a **hybridoma**, which had the immortality of the myeloma cell and the antibody-producing capacity of the normal B lymphocyte. The hybridoma cells were isolated from the fusion mixture and tested for production of the desired antibody. Those hybridomas able to produce the required antibody were then cultured individually, so that the cell cultures obtained arose from a single parent cell. Such cell cultures are described as *clones*, and monospecific antibodies obtained in this manner are known as **monoclonal antibodies**. The production of monoclonal antibodies is shown in Figure 3.1. Monoclonal antibodies have a well defined and reproducible antigen specificity and are also available indefinitely. Their use in diagnostic tests such as ELISAs (described below) gives these tests a very high degree of specificity.

The **fluorescent antibody technique** or **immunofluorescence,** as it is also called, can identify target pathogens or their molecules in a sample, in as little as 15 minutes. Cells from the sample material are first fixed to a microscope slide and then incubated with antibodies that bind the target, called *primary* antibodies. These antibodies have a special dye called a **fluorochrome** attached to them, which fluoresces (emits visible light) when exposed to uv, violet or blue light. A commonly used fluorochrome is fluorescein isothiocyanate (FITC), which glows yellow when irradiated with uv light.

After incubation with the fluorescent antibody, any unbound antibodies are removed by washing, and the slide is examined under the microscope while illuminated with a either a uv or other appropriate light source. Wherever the antigen is found, a fluorescent antibody will have bound, and this is revealed by the glow of its fluoro-chrome. The use of immunofluorescence in this manner is termed **direct immuno-fluorescence**, but an alternative technique, **indirect immunofluorescence**, may be

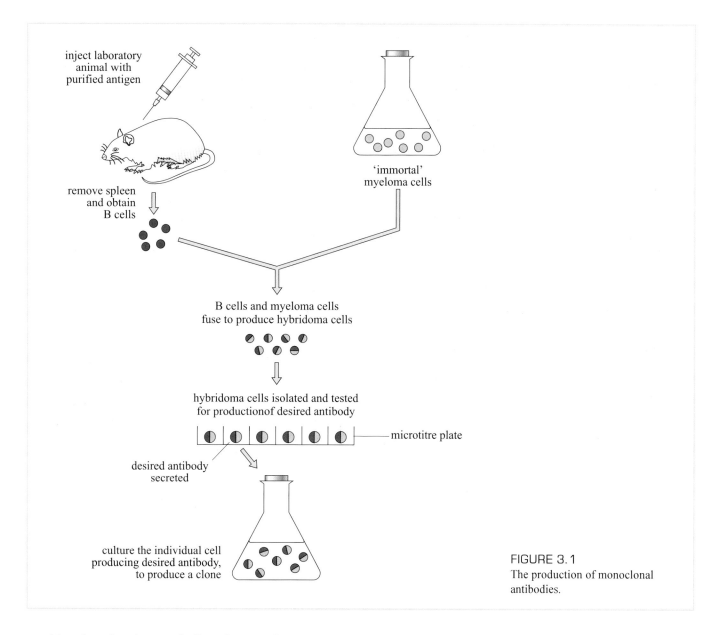

FIGURE 3.1
The production of monoclonal antibodies.

used in other situations. In indirect immunofluorescence, the fluorochrome is not attached to the primary antibody that recognizes the target antigen, but to a *secondary* antibody.

☐ Suggest why it is not always possible to attach the fluorochrome to the primary antibody.

◙ The binding of the fluorochrome might physically interfere with, and block, the binding between the antibody and the target antigen, giving a false negative result.

The secondary antibody is generally raised in a different species from that used to produce the primary antibody, and recognizes the constant regions of any antibodies made by the species that made the first antibody (see overleaf). This feature makes it more versatile, as it can be used as the fluorescent marker in a

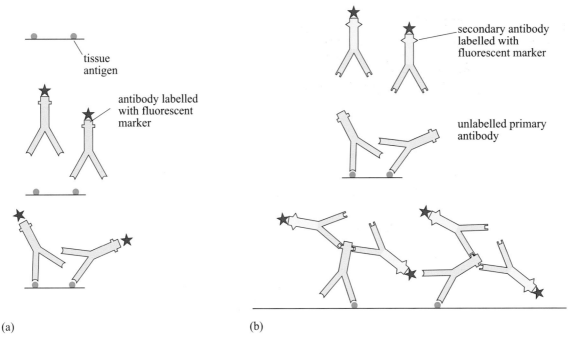

FIGURE 3.2 Immunofluorescence. (a) Direct immunofluorescence. (b) Indirect immunofluorescence.

whole range of diagnostic tests whose first antibodies are made by the same species. The extra distance provided by the second 'layer' of antibody means that the fluorochrome is unlikely to interfere with the binding of the primary antibody, and the test is therefore more accurate. Sensitivity can be increased by having several fluorescent secondary antibodies attached to each primary antibody, giving a much stronger fluorescent signal from each molecule of bound primary antibody.

The techniques of direct and indirect immunofluorescence are illustrated in Figure 3.2.

3.2 Enzyme-linked immunoabsorbent assay (ELISA)

The term **enzyme-linked immunoabsorbent assay** is such a mouthful that the technique is usually referred to by its acronym, **ELISA**. The ELISA procedure is summarized in Figure 3.3. It relies on the highly specific binding that occurs between an antibody and its epitope. A standard sample of target proteins or peptides prepared in the laboratory is fixed or adsorbed onto the solid wells in a microtitre plate. The patient's plasma or serum is then introduced into the wells of the microtitre plate, and any antibodies in the patient's blood that are specific for the target proteins will bind to these molecules attached to the well. The next step is to remove any unbound antibodies from the patient's sample, and this is achieved by gently rinsing, or 'washing' the wells with a suitable solution.

The next step uses a second, anti-human antibody. It is prepared by injecting material derived from human antibodies into a laboratory animal, to produce animal antibodies that bind human antibodies, called anti-human antibodies. When it is added to the wells of the microtitre plate, the anti-human antibody binds any human antibodies that it finds. Unbound anti-human antibody is then washed off as described above.

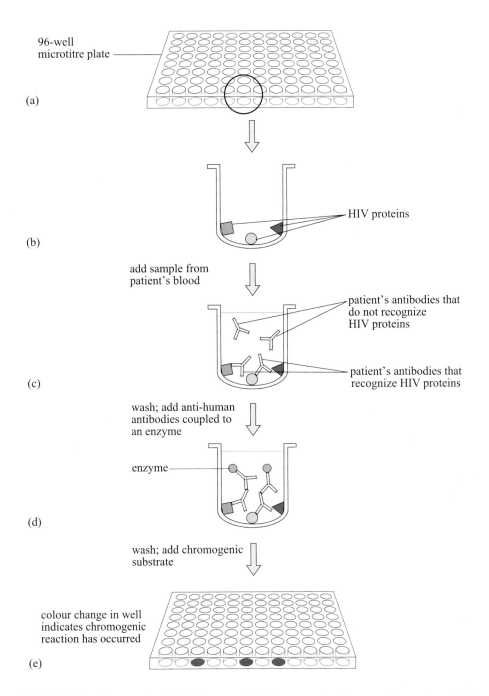

FIGURE 3.3 Diagram of an ELISA (enzyme-linked immunoabsorbent assay) procedure. (a) The assay is performed on a 96-well microtitre plate, but for simplicity we focus on just one well. (b) Prior to the assay, several different HIV proteins (shown here as different shapes) were adsorbed to the walls of the wells in the microtitre plate. (c) A sample of the patient's blood serum is added: any anti-HIV antibodies present bind the viral proteins. (d) Unbound antibodies are washed off and enzyme-linked anti-human antibodies are added. These bind to any human anti-HIV antibodies in the well. (e) Unbound anti-human antibodies are washed off. Then a chromogenic substrate is added, which is converted to a coloured product by the bound enzyme. The colour is detected on the microtitre plate. The presence of colour indicates that the patient has anti-HIV antibodies.

The anti-human antibody has another important property: there is an enzyme molecule covalently attached to it (hence the term *enzyme-linked* in the title of the assay). The enzyme acts on a *chromogenic* substrate; in other words, a colourless substance is converted to a coloured one by the action of the enzyme. By adding the chromogenic substrate to the microtitre wells, the presence of bound enzyme-linked antibody is revealed by a colour change. Since the enzyme-linked antibody is only present if the patient had antibodies in their blood against the target, the colour change indicates that the patient is positive for the disease under investigation.

The colour change just described can be seen by the unaided eye, but the intensity of the colour, and hence the amount of primary antibody bound, is measured using a machine called a *spectrophotometer*. The colour's intensity is proportional to the titre of antibodies in the patient's blood. A print-out showing the colour intensity for all the wells of the plate is normally obtained within a few minutes. The colour intensity is measured as a quantity known as *absorbance* (hence the term in the title), and the *immuno-* part of the title simply refers to the involvement of antibodies. ELISAs can be used both to detect specific antibodies in the patient's blood, as just described, or to detect pathogen-related *antigens*. In this case, the microtitre wells are coated with antibody to the target antigen, so if this antigen is present in the serum sample it will be bound by the antibodies in the well. Washing then removes all the unbound components of the serum. The enzyme is attached to another antibody that recognizes the target antigen, so the antigen is caught in an antibody sandwich. Detection is by a colour reaction, as before.

ELISAs are extremely sensitive, so a negative result requires no corroboration. However, the very sensitivity of the test means that false positives (Chapter 2) can occur, so a sample may be tested several times to check that the positive result is accurate. A second serum sample may also be tested to ensure that the final result is reliable. The commercial kits that have been developed for ELISAs are relatively expensive and beyond the reach of many countries. In addition, an ELISA requires a spectrophotometer, which is a costly piece of equipment.

3.3 Gel electrophoresis

Electrophoresis is the movement of charged molecules in an electric field. In an aqueous solution, the rate of migration of a molecule is determined by its shape and electrical charge. Gel electrophoresis, a widely used technique in molecular biology, allows the separation of proteins or nucleic acids. A gel, prepared as a liquid and allowed to set in an appropriate container, provides the support for the samples of material to be separated. The gel is transferred to a tank of buffer solution (to avoid changes in acidity during electrophoresis) and the samples loaded, typically into special wells formed by allowing the gel to set around the teeth of a 'comb' (see Figure 3.4). An electrophoresis tank has a wire electrode at each end; when connected to a suitable power supply these electrodes together produce a voltage across the gel. The gel itself has a network of pores, and this allows it to act a bit like a sieve, with the result that smaller molecules are able to pass through more quickly than larger molecules. The loaded samples therefore migrate through the gel at different speeds according to their net charge, shape *and* size. This means that the molecules are sorted into discrete bands, with their relative positions determined by these parameters.

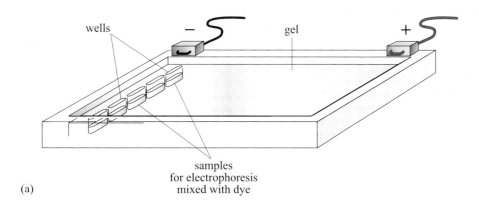

(a)

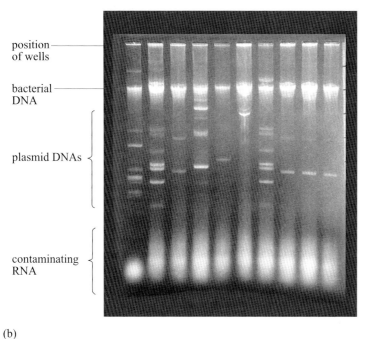

(b)

FIGURE 3.4 Gel electrophoresis. (a) The apparatus. (b) Photograph of the results of a gel electrophoretic analysis of plasmid DNA isolated from different samples of the bacterium *Klebsiella pneumoniae*. (This is called plasmid profiling and is one method for determining whether bacterial samples are of the same strain.)

In the example shown in Figure 3.4, gel electrophoresis has been used to separate plasmid DNA molecules extracted from different isolates of bacteria. DNA is negatively charged, so all the molecules migrate towards the anode (positive electrode), but their speed of migration is also determined by their size and shape. The DNA bands in the gel are invisible, so the gel has been stained with a dye that binds DNA and fluoresces under uv light. Photographing the gel under uv illumination produced the picture shown in Figure 3.4b.

Gel electrophoresis by itself is neither a particularly sensitive nor a specific test. However, its strength is that it separates molecules from each other, and the separated molecules can then be analysed further by *blotting* methods, as described below.

3.4 Blotting techniques

As mentioned above, electrophoresis can be used to separate protein or nucleic acid molecules from one another. Conditions for electrophoresis of the two types of molecule are different, and are explored below. The patient's sample is run on an electrophoretic gel to separate out the constituents (proteins or nucleic acids). The gel is then subjected to a further technique called blotting.

3.4.1 Nucleic acid blotting

Nucleic acids can be separated from each other by electrophoresis on agarose gels (agarose is a polysaccharide). Nucleic acids are often linear (although plasmids and some other small genetic elements are circular), and their charge to mass ratio is constant. Thus electrophoresis produces a pattern of bands that differ mainly in size.

Once bands have been established on the gel, they can be studied further if the gel is blotted. This can be accomplished in a number of ways, but typically a rather low-tech approach involving paper towels is used (see Figure 3.5a). The buffer is gradually drawn up through the apparatus, taking the nucleic acids along with it to the blotting filter or membrane, which is generally made of nitrocellulose. If DNA is to be transferred, then the gel is first washed to denature or separate the paired strands. Once the nucleic acids have been fixed to the nitrocellulose filter (in a pattern identical to the pattern of bands on the gel), they can be exposed to **DNA probes**. DNA probes are short pieces of single-stranded DNA (usually between 15 and a few hundred bases long) whose sequence or origins are known, and which are used to identify sequences complementary to themselves in other pieces of DNA or RNA. They work on the basis that single DNA strands, or a DNA and an RNA strand that are complementary to one another, can become hydrogen-bonded together in a process called **hybridization**. When a blotted filter is exposed to a DNA probe, the probe will bind to any sequences that it complements. After incubation, the blots are washed to remove unbound probe. The DNA probe has a coloured, fluorescent or radioactive marker attached, which allows the results to be easily assessed and specific sequences of DNA or RNA, complementary to the probe, to be located. When DNA is the molecule being probed, the technique is known as **Southern blotting**, after its inventor, Ed Southern (Southern, 1975). If RNA is the target, the technique is (flippantly) called **Northern blotting** – the same process, but for RNA instead of DNA.

3.4.2 Protein blotting

For proteins, the gel is made of polyacrylamide, and the buffers used during electrophoresis denature the proteins so that they all adopt a linear conformation, and are uniformly coated with a negative charge.

☐ Suggest why the proteins are subject to denaturation.

⬤ Electrophoresis separates molecules according to their shape, charge and size. Making the shape and the charge the same for all the protein molecules means that they are separated solely on the basis of size (their relative molecular mass).

The blotting procedure for proteins is the same as that described above for nucleic acids, and the result is shown in Figure 3.5b. However, when the molecule being

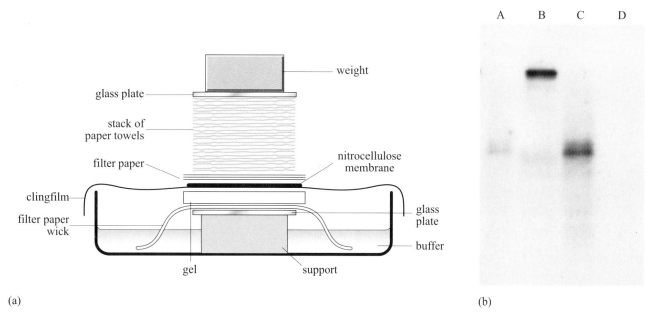

FIGURE 3.5 Blotting. (a) Apparatus. (b) Results of a Western blot. Lanes A and B are the test samples; lane C is a positive control and lane D is a negative control. Lane A shows a weak band at the same position as the marker band in lane C, so is positive. Lane B also shows a weak band near this position, but has a much stronger band at a higher molecular mass. This indicates that the test antibody recognizes not just the marker protein, but also another molecule of higher molecular mass.

probed is a protein, the technique is known as **Western blotting** (another point of the compass!), or **immunoblotting**, because the probe in this case is an antibody, raised against a specific epitope of interest. In Western blots there is an extra step after the first antibody probe, involving a second antibody linked to an enzyme, as in an ELISA.

☐ Look at Figure 3.5b, which shows the results for a Western blot test. Why does the negative control show no bands at all?

⬤ It shows no bands because no antigens recognized by the specific antibodies were included in this test.

Like ELISAs, blotting tests are expensive to carry out, and require sophisticated equipment. They are therefore not suitable in many parts of the less developed world, although they are quite commonplace in richer countries.

3.5 The polymerase chain reaction (PCR)

The polymerase chain reaction (PCR) is used when there are only very small quantities of target nucleic acid available. It is a very sensitive technique that you may have come across in the context of forensic medicine, where it is commonly used to identify the perpetrators of crimes who leave their own cells at the crime scene.

PCR can be used to copy, or amplify, a stretch of target DNA many times over. Short stretches of DNA, about 15–20 nucleotides long and called **primers**, are used to delineate the target sequence. The primers are synthesized artificially in a machine and are designed to be complementary to sequences at either end of the target sequence (see Figure 3.6a). The double-stranded DNA of the target sequence is denatured (the strands are separated) at the start of the PCR by heating it at around 95 °C. It is then allowed to cool to a temperature below about 65 °C, and at this temperature the primers are able to bind their complementary sequences – they *anneal* to them. The conditions are now provided for the synthesis of new daughter DNA strands, where each of the original target strands forms a template. The four deoxyribonucleoside triphosphates are provided, along with a DNA polymerase enzyme, and the temperature is increased to around 72 °C.

☐ What would you expect to happen to the DNA polymerase at this temperature?

⬤ The enzyme should be denatured and lose its activity.

In fact, the DNA polymerase that is used in PCR functions well at 72 °C, and is *not* denatured by the high temperatures used for denaturing the target DNA. One such enzyme, called *Taq* polymerase, is derived from the bacterium *Thermus aquaticus*, which lives in hot springs.

Once the synthesis of the daughter strands has occurred, these new double strands are denatured at 95 °C, and then allowed to anneal with the primers as before. Each strand from the previous reaction now becomes a template in a new round of DNA synthesis. Each round of denaturation, annealing and synthesis is described as one PCR cycle, and the target sequence that is copied is termed the PCR product (two PCR cycles are shown in Figure 3.6a). The conditions of the PCR cycle can be tailored to amplify particular DNA sequences (conditions may need to be varied depending on the length of the primers and the length and GC content of the target sequence). Typically 20–30 cycles are used for one reaction. The reactions are performed in small plastic tubes held in a machine called a thermocycler. Basically, this machine is able to heat up and cool down quickly, to provide the temperatures required for the PCR cycles. At the end of the reaction, a sample from each tube is analysed for PCR product, using gel electrophoresis. On the gel, PCR products show up as DNA bands.

The main problem with this technique is contamination by extraneous molecules of DNA. To monitor the situation, a negative control, containing all of the reaction mixture except the target DNA, is run alongside the other reactions. The negative control should not yield a PCR product: if it does then this means that at least one of the reagents is contaminated.

In rapid diagnosis, PCR can be used to detect the genomes of pathogens in clinical samples, even when they are present in only tiny amounts. This is because PCR amplifies the nucleic acid, by making many copies of it. However, PCR is used to amplify DNA, not RNA.

☐ How might PCR might be used to detect pathogens with *RNA* genomes?

⬤ A DNA copy that is complementary to the viral RNA genome, known as cDNA, must be synthesized first.

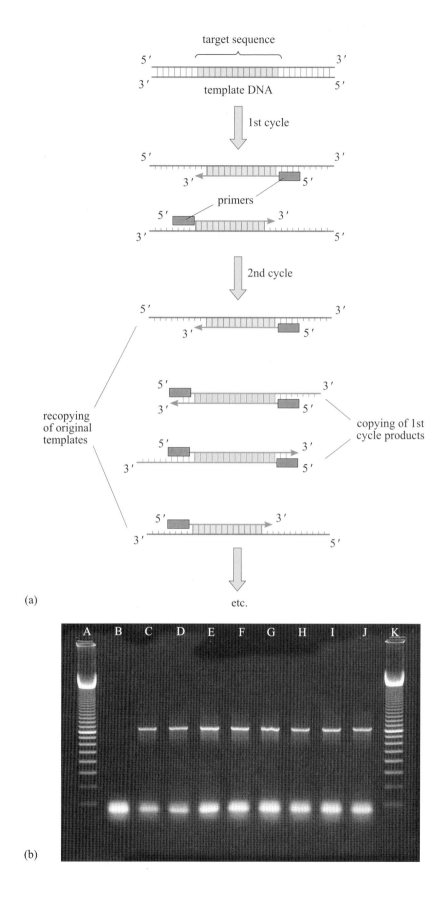

(a)

(b)

FIGURE 3.6

(a) The polymerase chain reaction (PCR). Sequence of steps in the process. See text for details.
(b) Photograph of the results. Lanes A and K contain molecular size markers or 'ladders', each band showing the position of nucleic acid of a known size. Lane B is a negative control, showing the results of a reaction in which all the PCR reagents were present, but no template DNA. Lanes C to J all show amplification of the target sequence (upper band), which was therefore present in the original samples. The lower band, present in lanes B to J, is the PCR product of an unrelated gene, which is included as a positive control in each lane to check that the reaction was working correctly.

This is achieved by using the enzyme reverse transcriptase (RT), before the main PCR reaction, in a process called RT–PCR. If viral RNA was present in the original sample then RT–PCR will produce a DNA product. On the other hand, if there was no viral RNA in the original sample, no DNA will be produced. Once the cDNA has been amplified, its nucleotide sequence may be determined in order to type the viral strain (see Section 4.3.2).

RT–PCR is not yet widely available, except in research and reference laboratories, but in UK diagnostic laboratories its use is gradually becoming more common.

4 DIAGNOSIS OF SOME IMPORTANT DISEASES

We now turn from the details of some diagnostic techniques to their application in practical laboratory diagnosis, and look at the extent to which the high-tech approaches can be modified or replaced for use in areas where the facilities are poor.

4.1 Diagnosis of cholera

The procedures used to diagnose cholera differ depending on whether the disease is endemic, epidemic or usually absent from an area. Where cholera is endemic or epidemic, laboratory diagnosis is not always appropriate, because immediate treatment of the patient is required and laboratory tests may take several days to complete. Since cholera is transmitted by the faecal–oral route, it tends to occur in areas without proper sanitation, and many of these areas are found in the developing world. The resources for the laboratory diagnosis of cholera may simply be unavailable in some of these areas, and because patients can be successfully treated without a laboratory diagnosis being made, this procedure is largely unnecessary (apart from supporting the conclusions of the clinical assessment). Where cholera is usually absent from an area, laboratory diagnosis is needed to confirm that a patient has the disease, partly since medical staff may be unfamiliar with the symptoms and partly because a positive identification must be made before any necessary control methods are initiated. Cholera is usually absent from developed countries, and these countries normally have a readily available laboratory service.

4.1.1 Areas where cholera is endemic or epidemic

The main symptom of cholera is profuse watery diarrhoea. The assessment of patients with diarrhoea has three stages:

1   First a history of the patient's disease is taken, including the details of any vomiting or fever, and their stools are examined by eye for blood, pus and mucus. The duration and consistency of the diarrhoea, and whether it contains blood, pus or mucus can point to the probable cause, for example the rice-water stools of cholera patients.

2   Next the patient is examined to assess the degree of dehydration they have suffered, so that the appropriate rehydration therapy can be started.

3   Diarrhoea patients, particularly children, are also examined for any underlying nutritional deficiency, so that a suitable feeding program can be administered. The malnutrition may have been caused by a cholera infection (if there is one), or by another disease such as pneumonia or measles.

After this initial assessment, laboratory investigations may be carried out, depending on the information already obtained and the epidemiology of diarrhoea in the locality.

In acute cholera, the watery nature of the stools means that the commensal flora of the bowel is much diluted, and the main bacteria present are cholera vibrios. These can be seen on examination of a wet mount of the stool under the microscope. They appear as curved rods, in contrast to the majority of faecal bacteria, which are straight rods. The identity of the bacteria can be confirmed as *Vibrio cholerae* by adding antiserum against the H antigen to the wet preparation of the stool.

☐ Recall the identity of the bacterial H antigen from your study of Book 2.

◼ The H antigens of a bacterium are its flagella.

H antiserum may be produced by injecting material containing a bacterium's flagella into a laboratory animal, waiting for an immune response to the antigen to occur, and then taking some of the animal's blood. The serum portion of the blood will contain antibodies that specifically bind that particular bacterium's H antigen. When *Vibrio cholerae* H antiserum is added to a wet mount of this bacterium, it will bind the organism's single polar flagellum.

☐ From the Cholera Case Study, can you predict what effect addition of the antiserum will have on the cholera vibrios?

◼ It will render them immotile, so bacteria that were swimming around in the wet preparation will become stationary.

The serotype can also be determined at this stage, by observing the immobilization of the vibrios with the addition of either Inaba or Ogawa antisera (see below).

4.1.2 Areas where cholera is usually absent

If a patient has a gastrointestinal disease then a faecal specimen is usually requested, and screened for the bacteria and parasites routinely isolated from such samples. In the UK *Vibrio cholerae* is not included among these bacteria and is only sought when the patient has recently travelled to an area where cholera is either endemic or epidemic.

Faecal specimens should be processed within three to four hours of receipt, otherwise they will require refrigeration at 4 °C. As you saw above, in the acute cholera patient, the faeces are so watery that the commensal flora is much reduced and *Vibrio cholerae* is the main bacterium present.

Growing the samples

From stool samples suspected of harbouring *Vibrio cholerae* a tiny portion (a bacteriologist's loopful) is taken and inoculated into a broth of alkaline peptone water (APW). Peptone water is a general-purpose medium that can be adapted for a variety of uses. If it is prepared using a phosphate buffer with a (weakly) alkaline pH of 8.4 (as APW), the cholera vibrios are able to grow, while the other faecal bacteria cannot, since this pH inhibits many bacteria. This selective action of APW significantly increases the number of *Vibrio cholerae* bacteria in the culture.

In the investigation of a suspected cholera case, the material from the APW enrichment broth is plated out on a type of solid selective medium called TCBS agar (thiosulphate–citrate–bile salts–sucrose) following an incubation period of six to eight hours. The selective agents in TCBS agar are the sodium thiosulphate, sodium citrate and the bile salts. These agents inhibit the growth of the majority of other Gram-negative bacteria that would otherwise grow from a faecal sample. *Vibrio cholerae* is also inhibited by this medium, but to a lesser extent than the other bacteria. The selectivity of TCBS is further increased by its high salt (NaCl) concentration and its pH of 8.6. Figure 4.1 shows the appearance of *V. cholerae* colonies on TCBS agar.

Bacterial colonies have a characteristic appearance on a particular agar, but sometimes different bacteria look very similar. Despite all the tailoring of TCBS to promote the growth of *Vibrio cholerae*, some other organisms do still manage to grow, and they can be distinguished from the vibrios by incorporation of indicators into the medium. The first indicator comprises sucrose and a pH indicator, bromothymol blue, which turns yellow at low pH. *Vibrio cholerae* uses sucrose as an energy source anaerobically, i.e. the bacterium *ferments* sucrose. When sugars are fermented in this way, acid is produced so the pH around the bacterial colony falls. This change in pH can be clearly seen, since it causes the pH indicator to change colour from blue to yellow, and this in turn changes the colour of the bacterial colony. The colonies of *V. cholerae* thus appear yellow, while the colonies of bacteria that are unable to ferment sucrose appear blue, since they are coloured by the unchanged bromothymol blue.

The second indicator detects the production of the gas hydrogen sulphide (H_2S), by turning the centre of the colonies black. Vibrios do not produce H_2S, but other organisms that grow on TCBS agar do, which makes them easily identifiable. You can see black and yellow colonies in Figure 4.1.

After overnight incubation, the yellow colonies on the TCBS agar without black centres are most likely to be *Vibrio cholerae*. They are now Gram-stained.

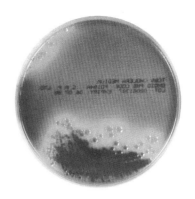

FIGURE 4.1
Appearance of *Vibrio cholerae* colonies on TCBS agar.

- ☐ What will be the appearance of the bacteria after Gram staining if the colonies are of *Vibrio cholerae*?

- ▣ The Gram stain will show Gram-negative bacilli, which may appear comma-shaped.

Testing the cultures

If the bacteria have this appearance, a pure culture is plated out onto a rich general-purpose agar (such as fresh blood agar: Table 2.2) and incubated for six to eight hours, in order to carry out further tests. The bacterial growth taken directly from the TCBS plate is unsuitable, since substances in the agar can affect the test results. The first test is a standard test used to distinguish between different species of bacteria, known as an **oxidase test**. Bacteria that can oxidize glucose to release energy have an electron transport chain similar to that used in respiration in our own mitochondria. This chain comprises various cytochromes and other enzymes, ending with the enzyme cytochrome oxidase. This enzyme can also oxidize tetramethyl-*para*-phenylenediamine hydrochloride (TMPD), more simply known as oxidase reagent, to produce a purple-coloured product in under ten seconds. *Vibrio cholerae* is oxidase-positive, so it quickly turns TMPD purple when a colony from the plate is brought into contact with it.

The final test for the colonies suspected to be cholera vibrios is the **slide agglutination test** (described below) to determine the group of their O antigens.

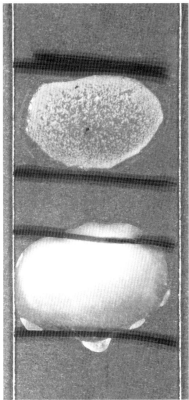

FIGURE 4.2
The slide agglutination test for *Vibrio cholerae*. A positive agglutination reaction is shown at the top. The test at the bottom, which remains smooth, is the negative control (test organism mixed with saline only).

○ Recall from the Cholera Case Study the groups of epidemic *Vibrio cholerae*.

● Group O1 is the main group of epidemic *V. cholerae*, but group O139 (Bengal) has also been responsible for epidemics in recent years.

Briefly, culture from a non-selective solid medium is suspended in sterile saline on a microscope slide and a small bacteriologist's loopful of test antiserum is added and mixed in by rocking the slide. If clumping occurs within one minute of mixing then agglutination has occurred, which means that the antibodies in the antiserum bind to the O antigen of the bacterium. Conversely, if clumping does not occur then there is no agglutination and the O antigen is not recognized by those particular antibodies. The slide agglutination test is illustrated in Figure 4.2.

If the organisms isolated from the TCBS plate that are oxidase-positive Gram-negative bacilli are group O1, they are presumptively identified as epidemic *Vibrio cholerae* O1. If this happens, then the authorities are usually informed since cholera is a notifiable disease in many countries, and member states of the WHO are required to report cases of the disease as part of the International Health Regulations.

The analytical profile index (API)

The identification is only presumptive at this stage, since the identity of any isolate cannot be confirmed without a series of further biochemical tests. In the past, these tests were performed individually, in a laborious fashion, using a variety of media. Nowadays pre-packaged tests, comprising small amounts of freeze-dried material held in separate wells on plastic strips, are used. A pure culture of the material to be identified is suspended in sterile distilled water, and a few drops of it added to each well. After overnight incubation, the results may be read. The API test (analytical profile index) is a popular version of these tests, where the test results are converted into a series of numbers. These numbers correspond to a particular species that can be identified by matching them up from all the API profiles (sets of numbers) available.

Any organism identified as presumptive *Vibrio cholerae* O1, is sent to a reference laboratory for confirmation, biotyping (as classical or El Tor) and serotyping. Remember that the biotypes are distinguished on the basis of their haemolytic activity, resistance to the antibiotic polymyxin B and their different susceptibilities to bacteriophage. The classical biotype can be further differentiated into the serotypes Inaba and Ogawa. These typing tests are important because *V. cholerae* O1 and non-O1 cannot be distinguished biochemically. Molecular methods have been developed for diagnosing cholera, using a variety of techniques (Hoshino *et al.*, 1998; Faruque *et al.*, 1997), but the main target of these methods is the gene encoding the A subunit of the cholera toxin (CT). These tests are not used on a routine basis in the UK, but are limited to reference and research laboratories.

4.2 Diagnosis of HIV infection

The methods used to diagnose HIV infection vary with the resources available, the local prevalence of the disease, the age of the patient and the stage the disease has reached. Although a few individuals may experience a glandular fever-like illness shortly after infection with HIV, most individuals do not seek medical advice unless they have reason to believe they have been infected or the symptoms of an AIDS-related condition appear. An initial assessment involves the medical practitioner taking a history and examining the patient. Risk factors, such as intravenous drug use and other sexually transmitted infections, are taken into account, and in industrialized countries, infection with HIV is confirmed by laboratory testing.

In the developing world, and those areas with fewer resources, such facilities may be few and far between. Under these circumstances HIV can be presumptively diagnosed as the underlying cause of persistent illness without laboratory support, although laboratory confirmation is always preferable.

4.2.1 Serological tests for HIV

Growing a virus in tissue culture is expensive and time-consuming, so like most tests for viruses, HIV tests are serological, in this case detecting blood-borne antibodies produced by the host against the virus, rather than detecting the virus itself. Paired sera to test for seroconversion (Section 2.3.2) are rarely available, but fortunately simply detecting anti-HIV antibodies in material from a patient is sufficient for a positive diagnosis. In countries that have a well funded health service, other tests for HIV are available that detect the viral genome or its proteins. These tests may be used for definitive diagnosis, but are more commonly used to monitor infected individuals during treatment, and as research tools. The character of the antibody response to HIV changes with time, as shown in Figure 4.3.

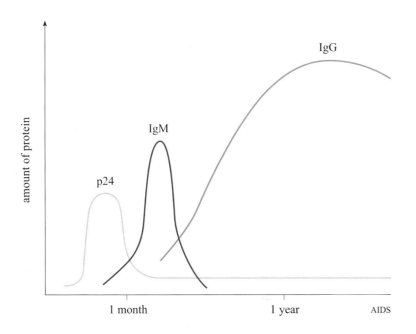

FIGURE 4.3
Antibody response to HIV infection. p24 is an HIV virion protein, and an increase in detectable p24 in a patient's serum indicates proliferation of the virus.

○ From Figure 4.3, which class of antibodies to HIV is produced first?

● The first antibodies are of the IgM class and are usually produced around three weeks following infection (although some antibodies can appear within a few day).

This pattern of antibody production means that a test for anti-HIV antibodies in the first few weeks of infection usually gives a negative result. Tests for anti-HIV antibodies normally detect IgG, but detection of these antibodies only indicates that infection with HIV has occurred at some time in the past, whereas detection of IgM shows that infection occurred recently. As you can see, the class of antibody detected, as well as the timing of the test, need to be taken into consideration when interpreting test results. This is especially so in very young babies, since the baby's antibody production is low immediately after birth and maternal IgG antibodies are present in the baby's circulation. IgG antibodies can cross the placenta from the maternal circulation during gestation and are also found in the colostrum, a milky fluid produced by the mother's breast, in the first two to three days after giving birth. If the mother is infected with HIV, her anti-HIV IgG antibodies will be in her baby's circulation, and the baby's blood may give a positive result if tested for anti-HIV antibodies. The result of such a test may be interpreted as meaning the baby is infected with HIV, but although the babies of HIV-infected women can themselves be infected with the virus, over half of the children born to these mothers do not carry HIV.

The main causative agent of HIV is HIV-1, and most tests detect antibodies to this agent rather than HIV-2, although tests can be adjusted to detect this less common variant. This might happen in West Africa for example, where HIV-2 is endemic.

4.2.2 ELISAs and Western blots

The initial test for HIV is an ELISA performed on nitrocellulose membranes rather than in a microtitre plate. If the ELISA result is definitely positive, then the diagnosis is confirmed using Western blotting. This is more specific (more able to correctly identify an uninfected person) and gives more detailed information. The confirmation of HIV diagnosis by Western blotting is illustrated in Figures 4.4 and 4.5.

The controls aid in interpreting the patient's results. The result is positive if the patient shows a colour change on two or more bands of the following proteins: p24, gp41, gp120 and gp160. If there is no clear result, then the test may be repeated.

☐ From the case study of HIV (Book 3), can you recall where on the virion the p24, gp41 and gp120 viral proteins are located? (Note that gp160 is a precursor of gp41 and gp120 and is not found on the mature virion.)

● p24 makes up the capsid of the virus core while gp41 lies in the viral envelope attached to gp120, which projects from the exterior surface of the viral envelope.

4.2.3 Low-cost options

As you saw above, ELISA and Western blotting are relatively expensive techniques, and beyond the reach of many countries. Some inexpensive laboratory tests have been developed that, in common with the ELISA and Western blotting, are based on HIV proteins fixed to a solid surface. Two examples of such tests are *particle agglutination* and *dot immunobinding* tests.

The particle agglutination test uses tiny beads made of polystyrene, latex or gelatin, which have been coated with viral proteins. These beads are incubated with various dilutions of a patient's serum in the wells of a microtitre plate, at room temperature,

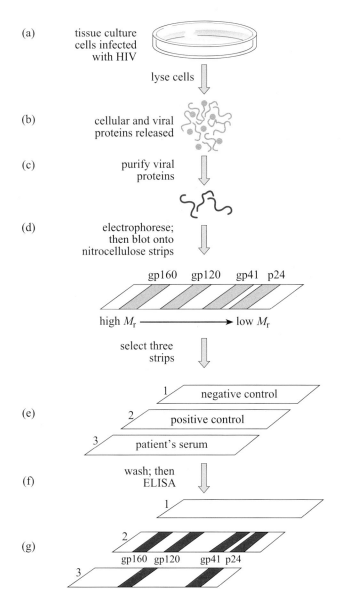

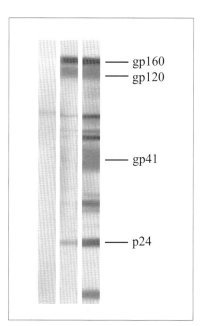

FIGURE 4.4 Protocol for confirmation of HIV diagnosis by Western blotting. (a) Tissue culture cells infected with HIV are grown in the laboratory. (b) The cells are then lysed to release the cellular and viral proteins. (c) The viral proteins are purified. (d) Electrophoresis is used to separate the viral proteins according to size, and the separated proteins are blotted onto nitrocellulose filter strips. (e) For each patient, three strips are selected: strip 1 (negative control) is incubated with serum from an uninfected individual; strip 2 (positive control) is incubated with serum from an HIV-infected individual; strip 3 is incubated with the patient's serum. (f) The strips are washed to remove unbound antibody. Then each is subjected to an ELISA procedure. (g) The results are interpreted as follows: strip 1 (negative control) shows no bands because no anti-HIV antibodies were present; strip 2 (positive control) shows that antibodies binding all four HIV proteins were present in this serum sample; strip 3 shows that antibodies binding HIV proteins gp120 and p24 are present in the patient's serum – a positive result.

FIGURE 4.5 Results from a Western blot test for HIV infection. The lane on the left is a negative control. The middle lane shows a weakly positive result, with gp160 and gp120 definitely present. The lane on the right is a strongly positive result, showing gp160, gp120, gp41, p24 and several other bands that are characteristic of HIV infection.

and the results compared to beads incubated with control sera. If the patient's serum contains anti-HIV antibodies, then a characteristic agglutination reaction is seen as a pale pink colour; conversely, if no anti-HIV antibodies were in the patient's serum, then a 'button' of beads that is dark pink in colour is found in the microtitre wells (much like a standard haemagglutination test). This test has a relatively low specificity, meaning that it is less able to correctly identify an uninfected person, and so is most appropriate for use in areas with a high prevalence of HIV infection.

○ Is the inability to correctly identify uninfected people likely to yield false positives or false negatives?

● False positives. They are identified as having the disease (i.e. as being infected with HIV) when in fact they are not infected.

The dot immunobinding test has viral antigens fixed to a comb or dipstick, which can be incubated with patient and control sera by dipping the comb or dipstick into the wells of a microtitre plate. This is followed by incubation in a reagent that changes colour in the presence of bound antibody. If a patient's serum contains anti-HIV antibodies, these will have bound to the viral antigens on the dipstick and their presence will be revealed by the colour change. This test can be used for diagnosing HIV infection, but is more commonly employed to screen blood for transfusions for the presence of this virus.

The fact that such tests use few reagents, which in some cases need no refrigeration, make them especially suited for developing countries. The tests are also very rapid, giving results in ten minutes, so patients are spared unnecessary journeys when travelling may be difficult.

4.3 Diagnosis of influenza

Many diseases produce symptoms similar to those of influenza; in fact, 'flu-like' is a term that is frequently used to describe a number of illnesses. Since influenza spreads rapidly by airborne transmission and is a life-threatening condition in certain vulnerable groups, it is important that cases of the disease are identified as quickly as possible, so that preventative measures may be taken. Most viral infections are untreatable, but the development of experimental antiviral drugs such as zanamivir (product name Relenza) means specific treatments for influenza may soon be available.

The influenza virus infects the respiratory tract and is spread by coughing and sneezing.

○ Which sites should be sampled for diagnosis?

● Specimens should be taken from the nose, throat or trachea.

In practice, the best specimens are nasal aspirates or washes, but swabs of the nose or throat may be used if they are taken vigorously enough to obtain cells. Ideally, samples should be taken within three days of the onset of illness, and all specimens need to be preserved in a transport medium and kept chilled by using ice packs, until they reach the clinical microbiology laboratory.

4.3.1 Identifying influenza virus

Antigenic viral components may be detectable in the sample upon its arrival, using immunofluorescence. This can identify influenza virus in the sample in as little as 15 minutes. Alternatively, the number of virions in the sample may be amplified, by culturing specimen material in tissue culture for 24 hours before performing the test. This 24-hour culturing procedure gives a greater chance of success in this test, but is no substitute for the usual week-long culture period required for the isolation of influenza virus from clinical specimens. However, a week may be too long in terms of patient management, and in some areas the facilities for cell culture may be unavailable. In these circumstances, evidence of infection may be obtained serologically, by observing a seroconversion. The comparison of two sera is especially important, because most people already have antibodies to influenza in their blood, from previous infections. Without the observed rise in antibody titre, the test may simply show that the patient has had influenza at some point in the past. Occasionally, a current influenza infection may provoke the production of antibodies that were originally made during a previous influenza infection, even though the current virus is a *different* strain and therefore antigenically distinct. This unpredictable immunological reaction makes interpreting the results of serological tests difficult, and is given the colourful name of 'original antigenic sin'.

Influenza has haemagglutinins protruding from its viral envelope, which it uses to attach to host cells prior to entry, and they can be detected by a haemagglutination test (Section 2.3.2). However, if the virus particles are incubated with antibodies specific for the haemagglutinin *before* the red blood cells are added, then the haemagglutination effect will be inhibited, since the haemagglutinins are no longer available to bind the red blood cell membranes, and these cells will form a pellet at the bottom of the tube, giving an apparently negative result. This is the principle behind the **haemagglutination inhibition test**, shown in Figure 4.6, where known cultures of virus are incubated with patient sera to determine whether haemagglutination will occur. If the patient has been infected with the same virus as that used in the test, their serum will contain antibodies that bind the viral haemagglutinin. This will

FIGURE 4.6
The haemagglutination inhibition test. See text for details.

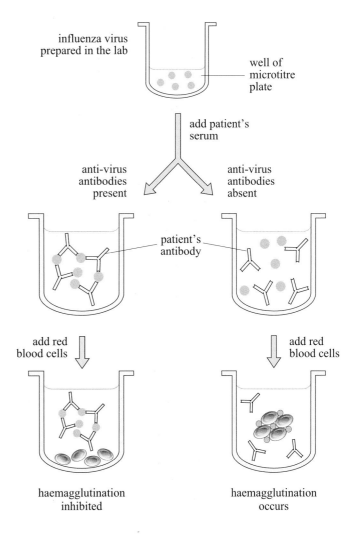

give a positive result, inhibiting haemagglutination when the red blood cells are added. If the patient has not been infected with the same virus, then the viral haemagglutinin will remain free of antibody and be available to haemagglutinate the red blood cells when they are introduced.

4.3.2 Typing of influenza

Influenza is one of the diseases monitored by the WHO's CSR programme (Section 2.4). The global surveillance of influenza involves 110 so-called sentinel laboratories in 82 countries. You can find details of this programme in the case study of influenza (Book 1, Section 2.3). The primary goal of this programme for influenza is 'to detect and identify newly emerging epidemic variants in a timely manner and to contribute to the selection of appropriate vaccine strains'. Here we are moving away from the care of the individual to a public health programme aimed at safeguarding whole populations. In order to carry out the work of this programme, it is essential that virus from patients is cultured in laboratory tissue culture or fertilized chicken eggs, so that definitive typing and subtyping of strains may be carried out. The WHO also monitor influenza in animals, but we will concentrate on influenza A virus derived from humans. This is characterized in terms of the particular variants of haemagglutinin (H1, H2, etc.) and neuraminidase (N1, etc.), which are components of the viral envelope.

Typing the haemagglutinin

A variety of techniques are used for typing influenza A, including ELISAs, but the WHO test of choice is the traditional method, which uses the haemagglutination inhibition test. This works on the principles set out above, but this time the virus from the patient is used and reference antisera are added. These antisera are prepared using purified haemagglutinin and neuraminidase and are monospecific, each antibody reacting only with one epitope. The exact haemagglutinin variant, e.g. H1, bound by each of these reference sera is known, so if a particular reference serum causes haemagglutination inhibition, then the type of haemagglutinin expressed by the virus must be the one that the antibodies in the reference serum recognize. In practice, these tests are carried out in parallel in microtitre plates.

Typing the neuraminidase

Typing influenza isolates in terms of their neuraminidase makes use of the enzyme activity of this glycoprotein in the **neuraminidase inhibition assay** (Figure 4.7). The neuraminidase cleaves sialic acid residues from the cell surface receptors of influenza virus. This reaction plays an important role for the virus in both access to and release from host cells. Antibodies that bind neuraminidase are known to contribute to immunity to influenza, and Relenza (see above), and another anti-influenza drug, Tamiflu (chemical name oseltamivir), are both able to inhibit neuraminidase action. There is further information about anti-influenza drugs on the Centers for Disease Control and Prevention (CDC) website (see Book 4 online resources).

The neuraminidase inhibition assay is performed in two parts. The first part determines the amount of neuraminidase activity in a patient influenza sample, as outlined in Figure 4.7a. A substrate (called fetuin) that has sialic acid residues is added to a sample of the influenza virus, and the neuraminidase enzyme cleaves the substrate to produce free sialic acid. Addition of a substance that inactivates the neuraminidase stops the reaction, and an indicator chromogen is added that turns

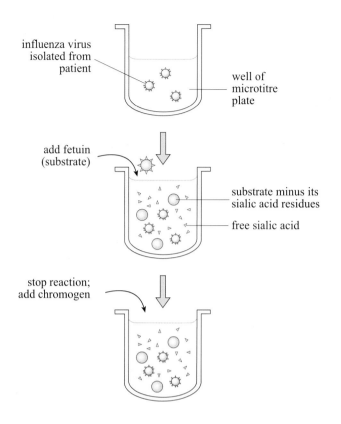

(a)

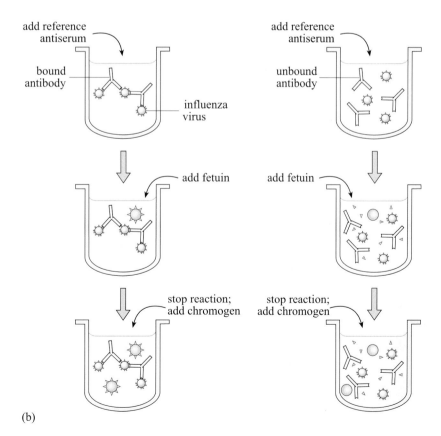

(b)

FIGURE 4.7
The neuraminidase inhibition assay.
(a) Assay of neuraminidase activity.
(b) The inhibition assay itself. See text
for details.

pink in the presence of free sialic acid. The intensity of the pink colour is proportional to the amount of free sialic acid and can be measured using a spectrophotometer. This assay of neuraminidase activity allows the appropriate amount of virus sample to be determined, and this quantity is then used in the second part of the assay. If too much or too little virus is used, the resulting changes, and therefore the neuraminidase, may be undetectable.

In the second part of the assay (Figure 4.7b), viral samples from the patient are incubated with reference antisera. Each of these reference antisera has antibodies that bind one particular neuraminidase variant, e.g. N1 or N2.

○ How can these antisera be used to type the neuraminidase variant?

● If the antibodies bind the neuraminidase in the patient's sample, they will inhibit its activity. This means that the patient's neuraminidase cannot cleave the sialic acid from its test substrate fetuin, so no colour change will occur when the chromogen is added. Conversely, if the antibodies in the reference antiserum do *not* bind the neuraminidase in the patient's sample, then the enzyme will remain uninhibited and the pink colour will be produced as before.

Use of PCR

PCR can be used both as a rapid method to diagnose influenza, and as a tool for typing the virus. In rapid diagnosis, RT–PCR (Section 3.5) is used to detect the RNA genome of influenza in clinical samples, even when the virus is present in only tiny amounts. Once the cDNA has been amplified, its nucleotide sequence may be determined in order to type the viral strain. However, as noted above, this technique is not yet used widely, even in developed countries.

4.4 Diagnosis of malaria

Malaria was endemic in Europe and the USA in the past (see case study of malaria in Book 1), and is still a cause for concern even in these countries today. In 1996, for example, around 10 000 reported cases of malaria were imported into the European Community, bringing with them the risk that malaria might re-emerge in this region. Malaria is still endemic in equatorial regions, and is now largely a disease of developing countries. In some of these countries, for example parts of sub-Saharan Africa, the transmission of malaria is described as *stable*, which means that individuals are bitten regularly by infected *Anopheles* mosquitoes and develop a high degree of immunity to the malaria parasites (*Plasmodium* spp.). In other areas, such as Southeast Asia, malaria transmission is described as *unstable*, which means that individuals are rarely bitten by infected mosquitoes and consequently develop little immunity to the malaria parasites.

4.4.1 Clinical diagnosis

The first step in diagnosing malaria is taking a history, including any recent travels and examining the patient. Often, the patient will have experienced fever, but this symptom is common for a variety of diseases. In fact, clinical diagnosis of malaria is difficult, unreliable, and may be complicated by other diseases that the patient is suffering from at the same time. However, it is the most widely used approach and may be all that is available in some areas. The symptoms vary depending on the degree of immunity that a person has to the parasite, the stage of the disease and the person's age. In stable areas, children under the age of five and pregnant women are the most likely victims, whereas in unstable areas, all groups of the community can be affected. Different species of *Plasmodium* produce different symptoms: for example, the frequency of the fevers is a unique characteristic of a particular species. As you will recall from the malaria case study, all of the malaria parasites can cause uncomplicated malaria, but *P. falciparum* can produce complicated and severe malaria, which is a life-threatening condition. It is particularly likely to spread to the brain and cause death in young children. The diagnosis of malaria must therefore be fast and accurate, so that appropriate treatment may be given and fatalities averted. If life-threatening malaria is suspected on clinical examination, such is the danger that treatment is begun immediately, and confirmation of the diagnosis sought later.

4.4.2 Laboratory diagnosis

Malaria can only be definitively diagnosed by laboratory testing, which usually comprises the detection of asexual parasites in a peripheral blood sample examined under the microscope. (A peripheral blood sample is one obtained from the periphery of the body, e.g. the ear or finger.) The sample is taken before any antimalarial drugs are given to the patient, usually by pricking their finger. Drops of blood are placed directly onto a microscope slide to give both a thick film (comprising several large drops) and a thin film (composed of one small drop, which is heat-fixed), as shown in Figure 4.8.

The thick film is allowed to dry in the air and is then stained with Giemsa or Field's stain. Staining unfixed red blood cells in this manner causes them to undergo haemolysis (lysis of red blood cells), so on viewing, just their empty cell membranes or 'ghosts' can be seen. This allows the parasites to be seen easily, despite the thickness of the film. Use of a thick film allows a large volume of blood to be examined for the malaria parasites, and provides quantitative evidence concerning the the number of parasites in the patient's blood. These thick films are sensitive, allowing as few as five parasites per microlitre to be detected, and 200 different views or fields of the film are examined before a negative diagnosis can be made.

The thin film is fixed and stained with Giemsa, a standard stain for blood, which acts mainly on white blood cells to turn nuclei blue and cytoplasm pinkish. Thin films take around ten times longer to examine than thick films, and so are not used for routine diagnosis, but they do allow the species of *Plasmodium* parasite (see case study on malaria in Book 1 for details) to be identified. The trophozoites, schizonts and gametocytes of the four *Plasmodium* species that cause malaria can be distinguished microscopically, and the stages seen provide information on disease prognosis. The appearance of the infected red blood cells, which may change size, shape, colour or develop particular markings (called Schüffner's stippling) also differs from species to species.

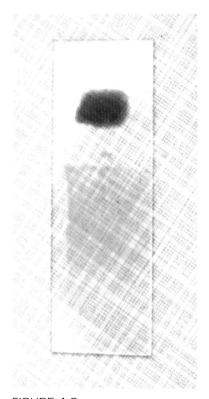

FIGURE 4.8
A thick film of blood (top) and a thin film (bottom) used for the microscopic diagnosis of malaria.

◯ Will the red blood cells on a thin film be intact or haemolysed?

◖ Intact, because the cells have been fixed to the microscope slide, prior to staining.

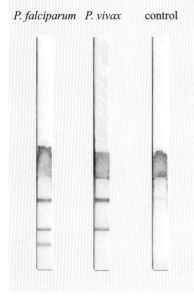

P. falciparum   P. vivax   control

FIGURE 4.9
Results of a dipstick test for malaria.
The figure shows three dipsticks, all
with a broad (positive control) band
showing that the tests have worked.
The negative control shows no other
bands, but the samples containing
Plasmodium give rise to a banding
profile characteristic of the particular
species present.

Identifying the *Plasmodium* species is crucial, since it will allow the risk to the patient to be assessed and the most appropriate treatment to be chosen.

An alternative way to examine blood is using fluorescence microscopy, where the DNA and RNA within the parasites are stained with a fluorochrome (Section 3.1). This is an easier and faster way to detect the parasites than examining a thick film, but cannot reliably detect *Plasmodium* spp. if there are fewer than 100 parasites per microlitre, which is quite a heavy infestation. It is also quite expensive, purely qualitative and less discriminating between species, so is not widely used in the field.

Interpreting blood films requires time, expertise, appropriate reagents and a relatively expensive microscope. If such resources are unavailable, some cheaper, easier alternatives can be used, such as a dipstick test, which is illustrated in Figure 4.9. This test requires little skill and gives results within 10–15 minutes. It is based on antibody–antigen interactions and detects antigens specific to *Plasmodium* in a patient's blood. This test allows different *Plasmodium* species to be distinguished, but does not provide quantitative information.

Molecular methods, such as PCR, have been developed for *Plasmodium* spp., but they are not suitable for routine diagnosis. They are more often employed for epidemiological research and patient screening in specialist laboratories.

4.5 Diagnosis of schistosomiasis

In common with malaria, schistosomiasis is a disease that mainly affects developing countries, although imported cases of both diseases do occur in developed nations (Book 2, Section 7.3.1). In such cases, the greatest obstacle in diagnosis is in considering a parasitic infection in the first place.

In areas where schistosomiasis is common, a clinical examination may be sufficient to diagnose the disease. Urinary schistosomiasis is more easily identified, and infection with *Schistosoma haematobium* is usually accompanied by blood in the urine, which may be present in very small amounts (described as microhaematuria). Usually though, laboratory tests are required to confirm the diagnosis. The gold standard for schistosomiasis diagnosis is observing the worm eggs in clinical samples.

- What samples should be taken to diagnose schistosomiasis?

- For urinary disease, a urine sample is appropriate; for intestinal disease, a faecal sample is taken.

Urine is often filtered first to separate the eggs from the liquid, which concentrates them and makes them easier to find (see Figure 4.10). Another important type of specimen for diagnosing schistosomiasis is a biopsy. For suspected infections with *Schistosoma mansoni* and *S. japonicum*, rectal biopsies the size of a grain of rice are taken. If infection with *S. haematobium* is thought to be the culprit, then a bladder biopsy may be obtained. The biopsy material is cleaned with water and then pressed between glass until it is transparent. On examination of this preparation, any worm eggs present will be easily visible.

(a)　　　　　　　　　　　　　　　　(b)

FIGURE 4.10 Urine filtration test for schistosomiasis. (a) A urine sample is passed through a filter that retains worm eggs. (b) The eggs are detected by examining the filter under the microscope.

The examination for eggs is highly specific, provides quantitative evidence concerning the infection, and is both cheap and simple. There are disadvantages, however: it can be time-consuming, and if infection rates in a community are low, then several samples may be needed for a reliable diagnosis. Providing faecal samples may be culturally unacceptable in some areas, resulting in low levels of patient cooperation. Finally, the extent of the disease is more readily assessed by examining the patient, rather than their faeces and urine. In recent years, ultrasound has been employed to monitor the pathology associated with schistosomiasis infection, and the biopsy procedures described above also allow the mucous membranes of the bladder or rectum to be examined. However, these techniques require fairly sophisticated equipment, so are not available in all areas.

Serological methods of diagnosis have been developed with differing degrees of success. Detection of the antibodies provoked by the infection is possible, but the titre of antibody measured is generally unrelated to the worm burden of a patient. The high titre that results from a new infection with few worms has been a useful tool in identifying recent cases, but apart from this role, antibody detection has not been found to be very helpful in diagnosing the disease.

In the past decade, great strides forward have been made with tests to detect specific worm antigens. Two gut-associated antigens known as circulating anodic antigen (CAA) and circulating cathodic antigen (CCA) have attracted most interest, and are easily detected in urine and serum samples. (The antigen names are based on their electrophoretic behaviour.) The tests take the form of ELISAs, so they are quite expensive and are not appropriate in field settings away from the laboratory.

Their strength is that they provide reliable quantitative data from a single sample, and the CAA level has been found to correlate well with the size of the worm burden. The drawbacks of using ELISA may be overcome with one of the latest developments in this field, which is a one-step assay that detects CCA in urine in a matter of minutes. The assay is performed using a strip of material that has been impregnated with the appropriate reagents.

CONCLUDING REMARKS

In this book we have attempted to show the importance of, and some of the difficulties of achieving, accurate diagnosis of infectious diseases. The existence of the WHO notification system, and other national surveillance programmes and reference laboratories, emphasizes that the threat of epidemics remains a global problem. Although modern science can improve the sensitivity and specificity of diagnostic tests, these improvements are likely to be of benefit only to richer countries, at least in the short term. Only when rapid, accurate, simple and above all cheap tests for the major global infectious diseases become available can we truly say that we have made a difference to the majority of sufferers.

LEARNING OUTCOMES

When you have studied this book and the associated video sequence and case studies, you should be able to:

1 Define and use, or recognize definitions and applications of, each of the terms printed in **bold** in the text. (*all questions*)

2 Explain, using examples, why accurate diagnosis is important for both the individual patient and the wider population. (*Question 1*)

3 Outline the steps that occur between the time when a patient reports feeling ill and the time when an appropriate therapy is administered. (*Question 2*)

4 Explain, using examples, why diagnosis by a clinician may not be straightforward. (*Questions 1 and 2*)

5 Describe the major techniques used for diagnosis, and outline the theoretical basis behind them. (*Question 5*)

6 List the reasons for using aseptic technique, and outline the main processes involved. (*Question 4*)

7 Explain the differences between low-tech and high-tech laboratory diagnostic methods, and explain differences in their geographical availability. (*Question 3*)

8 For named diseases, list the main techniques used for diagnosis and relate their availability to their degree of sophistication. (*Question 6*)

QUESTIONS

Question 1

A displaced person arrives at a refugee camp and complains of severe diarrhoea. Briefly suggest what diagnostic tests might be carried out, and any public health measures that should be adopted in the refugee camp.

Question 2

Your child complains of a headache and has a rash on their chest. Assuming you live in a developed country with health advice readily available, describe the events that might take place to help your child recover.

Question 3

Of the following seven diagnostic techniques, state which are 'high-tech' and which are 'low-tech'.

ELISA   broth culture

Gram staining   haemagglutination test

taking a history   antibiotic sensitivity testing

PCR

Question 4

Why is it necessary to flame the necks of bottles when transferring microbial material in and out of them?

Question 5

Suppose you are a medical laboratory technician in a well-equipped and funded laboratory. What tests would you carry out on samples from a patient with a respiratory disease?

Question 6

Complete the table below by giving examples of the organisms that can be identified by the techniques listed.

Technique	Organisms identified
acid-fast staining	
TCBS agar	
ELISA	
PCR	
slide agglutination test	
Gram staining	
Western blotting	
urine filtration	

ANSWERS TO QUESTIONS

QUESTION 1

There are many causes of diarrhoea, and distinguishing between them may be difficult. A history should be taken from the patient, detailing any food they have recently eaten, and any contact with other people with diarrhoea. A visual examination of the stools might suggest a diagnosis: e.g. blood in the stools might mean infection with enterohaemorrhagic *E. coli*, whereas rice-water stools would suggest cholera. There are unlikely to be any laboratory facilities available in a refugee camp, so the patient should be isolated as far as possible from others, and strict hygienic measures applied to them. In particular, their faeces should be prevented from contaminating the drinking water. Since dehydration is a problem with all cases of diarrhoea, attempts should be made to have a rehydration solution available to any sufferers. If vaccination measures are available, they should be offered initially to vulnerable groups (the young and the elderly) and then, if resources permit, to everybody.

QUESTION 2

As an anxious parent you would probably begin by taking your child to the family doctor. The doctor would examine the child to assess her symptoms, and would take a history from you both to establish whether you had recently travelled to an area with particular endemic diseases, or been in contact with infected persons. This information, together with features like the appearance and location of the rash, would allow the doctor to make an initial diagnosis. The doctor's initial diagnosis might also depend on their knowledge of any current local epidemics, such as measles in local schools. If the doctor was confident in diagnosing a straightforward childhood illness, you would be sent home with appropriate therapeutic advice, to wait for your child to recover. However, in less certain cases the doctor could take samples to send to the local clinical microbiology laboratory, making sure they were labelled correctly. If a bacterial infection was suspected, the laboratory would culture the samples using non-selective and selective media, and would assess the antibiotic sensitivity profile of any identified pathogen. This information would be conveyed back to the doctor, who could then quickly prescribe a suitable antibiotic. For non-bacterial diseases the culture period would be longer, and therapy might begin before the diagnosis was finalized (this might happen anyway if the child was seriously ill). If the infection was notifiable, the laboratory would contact the authorities.

QUESTION 3

High-tech: ELISA, PCR.

Low tech: Gram staining, taking a history, broth culture, haemagglutination test, antibiotic sensitivity testing.

QUESTION 4

Microbes are readily carried in tiny droplets in aerosols, and can easily spread to the environment. Flaming the necks of bottles in a Bunsen flame causes an updraft which carries away any aerosols and microbes. As the microbes are carried into the flame by the updraft, they are destroyed, thus protecting both the operator and the surroundings from microbial contamination.

QUESTION 5

In the absence of any further information about the patient, you do not know whether the suspected cause of the infection is viral (e.g. influenza), bacterial (e.g.TB) or something more unusual. Being pragmatic, you would test for the more obvious things first.

To test for influenza you could try to identify viral antigens in the sample by immunofluorescence. You might also carry out a haemagglutination test. If the presence of influenza virus was confirmed, you could identify the type by doing a haemagglutination inhibition assay and a neuraminidase inhibition assay.

To test the sample for TB, the first approach is to analyse the sample microscopically. You could try to detect TB bacilli by fluorescence microscopy, or you could do a Ziehl–Neelsen stain to identify any mycobacteria in the sample. A positive identification by Ziehl–Neelsen is conclusive, but you might also wish to identify mycobacterial DNA by PCR analysis. *Mycobacterium tuberculosis* is difficult to grow in culture, and needs to be grown in egg-based media. The cultures are very slow-growing, so screening for drug resistance is a slow process.

If neither of these approaches yielded a firm diagnosis, you would look further afield, and culture any microbes in the patient's sample on a non-selective medium. Any that grew, and were not part of the normal flora, could then be selectively cultured, and, hopefully, identified.

QUESTION 6

There are several possible answers to this question; we list only some of them in the table below.

Technique	Organisms identified
acid-fast staining	mycobacteria
TCBS agar	*Vibrio cholerae*
ELISA	many, including schistosomes
PCR	many, including *Plasmodium* spp.
slide agglutination test	bacteria with specific O antigens
Gram staining	Gram-positive and Gram-negative bacteria
Western blotting	many, including HIV
urine filtration	*Schistosoma haematobium*

REFERENCES

Archibald, L. K. and Reller, L. B. (2001) Clinical microbiology in developing countries, *Emerging Infectious Diseases*, **7**(2), pp. 302–305.

Brown, T. A. (1989) *Genetics: a Molecular Approach* (2nd edn), Chapman and Hall, London.

Faruque, F. M., Ahmed, K. M., Siddique, A. K., Zaman, K., Alim, A. R. and Albert, M. J. (1997) Molecular analysis of toxigenic *Vibrio cholerae* O139 Bengal strains isolated in Bangladesh between 1993 and 1996: evidence for emergence of a new clone of the Bengal vibrios, *Journal of Clinical Microbiology*, **35**, pp. 2299–2306.

Flint, S. J., Enquist, L. W., Krug, R. M., Racaniello, V. R. and Skalka, A. M. (2000) *Principles of Virology*, ASM Press, Washington DC.

Gilbert, G. L. (2002) Molecular diagnostics in infectious diseases and public health microbiology: cottage industry to postgenomics, *Trends in Molecular Medicine*, **8**, p. 280.

Greenwood, D., Slack, R. and Peutherer, J. (eds) (2000) *Medical Microbiology* (15th edn), Churchill Livingstone, London.

Hoshino, K., Yamasaki, S., Mukhopadhyay, A. K., Chakraborty, S., Basu, A., Bhattacharya, S. K., Nair, G. B., Shimada, T. and Takeda, Y. (1998) Development and evaluation of a multiplex PCR assay for rapid detection of toxigenic *Vibrio cholerae* O1 and O139, *FEMS Immunology and Medical Microbiology*, **20**(3), pp. 201–207.

Hawkey, P. M. and Lewis, D. A. (eds) (1989) *Medical Bacteriology: a Practical Approach*, IRL Press at Oxford University Press, Oxford.

Heritage, J., Evans, E. G. V. and Killington, R. A. (1996) *Introductory Microbiology*, Cambridge University Press, Cambridge.

McCormick, A. (1993) The notification of infectious diseases in England and Wales, *Communicable Disease Report*, **3**, R19.

Mims, C., Playfair, J. and Roitt, I. (1998) *Medical Microbiology* (2nd edn), Mosby International Limited, London.

Prescott, L. M., Harley, J. P. and Klein, D. A. (1999) *Microbiology* (15th edn), WCB McGraw-Hill, London.

Southern, E. M. (1975) Detection of specific sequences among DNA fragments separated by agarose gel electrophoresis, *Journal of Molecular Biology*, **98**, pp. 503–517.

WHO Fact Sheet No. 200 (June 1998), *Global Infectious Disease Surveillance*, World Health Organization, Geneva.

WHO/USAID Joint informal consultation report (October 1999) *New Perspectives: Malaria Diagnosis*, World Health Organization, Geneva.

ACKNOWLEDGEMENTS

The authors would like to acknowledge the help of Dr Michael Carter of the UK Public Health Laboratory Service in the preparation of this text.

Grateful acknowledgement is made to the following sources for permission to reproduce material in this book:

Cover image: Dr Linda Stannard, UCT/Science Photo Library.

Figures 1.1, 4.10a, 4.10b: WHO/TDR/Crump; *Figure 2.3a*: Wellcome Photo Library/Tropical Medicine; *Figure 2.3b*: 'Biohazard Sign.' Crown copyright material is reproduced under Class Licence Number CO1W0000065 with the permission of the Controller of HMSO and the Queen's Printer for Scotland; *Figure 2.5*: Basler, C. and Palese, P., Mount Sinai School of Medicine of the City University of New York; *Figures 3.1, 3.6a*: Mimms, C. *et al*., Non-cultural techniques ..., Figs 14.13 and 14.14, *Medical Microbiology*, 2nd edn, copyright © 1998, Mosby International Limited; *Figure 3.2*: Roitt, I. *et al.* (2002) Antigen–antibody interactions, Fig. 27.8, *Immunology*, 6th edn, Elsevier Science Limited; *Figures 3.4, 3.6b*: Courtesy of Laura Hibberts; *Figure 3.5b*: Courtesy of Ignacio Romero/Open University; *Figures 4.1, 4.2, 4.5*: Wellcome Photo Library/Tropical Medicine; *Figure 4.3*: Serological tests for HIV infection–1, HIV/AIDS: Diagnosis and Monitoring Screen 18, © The Welcome Trust; *Figure 4.8*: L. J. Bruce-Chwatt, TMR/Wellcome Photo Library; *Figure 4.9*: TMR/Wellcome Photo Library.

Every effort has been made to trace all the copyright owners, but if any has been inadvertently overlooked, the publishers will be pleased to make the necessary arrangements at the first opportunity.

INDEX

Note: Entries in **bold** are key terms. Page numbers referring to information that is given only in a figure or caption are printed in *italics*.

W

Western blotting 33

    HIV testing 42, *43*

wet mounts 21

World Health Organization (WHO), Communicable Disease Surveillance and Response system 11, 46

Y

yellow fever, notifiable disease 11

Z

zanamivir *see* Relenza

Ziehl–Neelsen stain 21

zone of inhibition 21